Rainy Day Activities

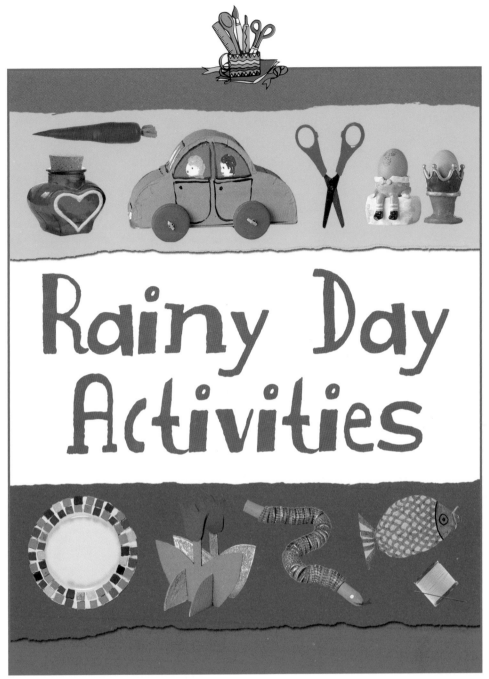

Rainy Day Activities

Vivienne Bolton

p

This is a Parragon Book
This edition published in 2004

Parragon
Queen Street House
4 Queen Street
Bath BA1 1HE, UK

Produced by Miles Kelly Publishing Ltd

British Library Cataloguing-in-Publication Data
A catalogue record for this book is available from the British Library

ISBN 1-40543-837-1

Printed in China

The publishers would like to thank Inscribe Ltd., Bordon, Hants.
for providing the art materials used in these projects and
Sophie Boulton for her assistance.

Contents

How to Use this Book

This book is filled with ideas for hand-crafted models, toys, useful gifts, and games. You will need a sturdy pair of scissors and good PVA glue, tape, and a set of paints. Most of the crafts can be made from recycled materials from around the house. Some projects are made using natural materials such as twigs, leaves, and pebbles. It is a good idea to save empty boxes, attractive pieces of coloured paper, and other useful items for future use.

The introduction is full of interesting information and inspirational ideas for further projects.

Each project has a list of things that you will need. Check through the list before you begin to make sure you have all the materials and equipment ready.

All the photographs in this book have been carefully taken to illustrate as many ideas as possible.

SWEET JAR AND P

Bottle Ga

Create a miniature oasis in a bottle. All you need to start a bottle garden is a large, empty sweet jar and some potting compost. Choose plants which will stay quite small; ask for assistance at your local garden centre or florist. Some garden centres have bottle garden departments where they sell small plants suitable for this enclosed, small environment. Bottle gardens should never have the sun shining directly

onto them (
they do need
the soil mois
often if the li
bottle garden
summer. Dece
outliners. Cho
pattern or use
paint to create
exterior of the

You will need:

Sticks
Old spoon
Wire
Kitchen sponge
Cotton wool
A large empty sweet jar
Pebbles or gravel
Suitable potting compost
Suitable plants
Glass paints outliner
Glass paint

28

The icon at the top of each page tells you what topic is being covered. Here the acorn tells you this is a nature project.

Step-by-step instructions will guide you through each project.

Some of the projects have a Tips and Warnings box. Read these at the start of the project.

ens

t too hot), but
ht situation. Keep
t need to water
ly on. Feed your
eks during the
glass paints and
tliner for a stylish
r and coloured
s effect on the

1 Begin by making some suitable bottle garden tools. For a digging tool, use an old spoon attached with wire to a long stick. Use a piece of kitchen sponge wired onto a stick to press the earth down when you are planting. Lastly, you will need a cleaning tool. For this use a piece of cotton wool wired onto a stick (you may need a few of these to tidy up the bottle garden once it is planted).

2 Place a thin layer of pebbles or gravel in the base of the bottle. This will provide drainage for the bottle garden plants.

3 Cover the pebbles with a thick layer of potting compost. Press the compost down gently using your sponge tool.

4 Use the digging tool to place individual plants in position. Press the compost down firmly around the plants, taking care not to damage their roots.

5 Use the cotton wool tool to clean up the sides of the bottle garden. Wipe away any smears or pieces of compost that have stuck to the sides of the jar.

6 Your bottle garden is now ready to decorate. Choose a simple pattern and mark it out with the outliner. The stained glass effect will resemble a mini-conservatory.

When choosing plants for your bottle garden choose low growing varieties. Keep the compost moist but do not overwater. Feed your bottle garden every two weeks in the growing season.

Nature

Seedpod Jewellery

Collect seedpods and hollow stalks from the garden in the summer, and stand them up in a jar to dry in a warm airy spot. You will need a large darning needle to make a hole through the seedpods once they have dried. The beads in the necklaces are made from cut lengths of dried stalks. Thread them using the darning needle and decorate them with paint. Gold and brown paint have been used on these beads to accentuate the natural look. Beads painted in bright colours and decorated with glitter would make an attractive necklace.

You will need:

Selection of seedpods and stalks

Scissors

Paint

Paint-brush

Darning needle

Thread

Felt tip pens

Elastic band

Check with an adult before you pick plants and stems to dry.

1 To make this necklace you will need a few dried hollow plant stems, some small fir-cones and seedpods. Begin by cutting the plant stems into bead-size lengths. Paint the bead lengths, fir cones and seedpods gold. When your beads are dry use the darning needle to make suitable holes through them and thread together using one seedpod to every three plant stems to make a necklace or bracelet.

2 This delicate looking necklace is made simply from some dried hollow plant stems. Once you have cut the stems into bead-sized lengths, decorate the beads using brown felt tip pens or brown paint. Thread them together using the darning needle.

3 A small bunch of twigs is used to make this pendant. Choose straight twigs that don't have any thorns or snags. Use an elastic band to hold them together in a neat bunch to form a pendant. Paint the pendant gold; it may be necessary to give it two coats. Once the paint had dried attach a length of thread to the pendant and it is ready to wear.

Birdbath

This mosaic bird bath would make a good rainy day project. You could use bought miniature tiles or make your own from oven bake clay like we have. If you make your own tiles you will need to work out the number needed plus a design and colour scheme. You could take some inspiration from the colour scheme in your garden. Use a tin bowl with a wide lip or ledge for the mosaic pattern. Broken china plates can be recycled to use as mosaic decoration, but do ask an adult to assist as the edges can be quite sharp. A mosaic decorated plate would also look good as a houseplant saucer.

You will need:
Oven bake clay

Rolling pin and knife

Metal plate

Plastic gloves

Spatula

Grout

Cloth

Varnish

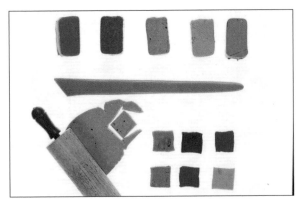

1 Begin by making the tiles using oven bake clay. Roll out the clay on a clean work surface with the small rolling pin. Cut square tile shapes in your chosen colours to fill the rim of the plate. Harden the tiles in the oven according to the manufacturer's instructions.

2 When the tiles are ready, make a rough plan of how you will lay them on the plate edge. You will need a metal or china soup plate with a wide raised edge. Put on the plastic gloves and use the spatula to spread a layer of tile grout across the edge of the plate.

3 Press each tile gently into the grout. Leave a narrow space between each tile. You will fill this later. Make sure the tiles all lie neatly along the edge of the plate. Leave to set for 24 hours.

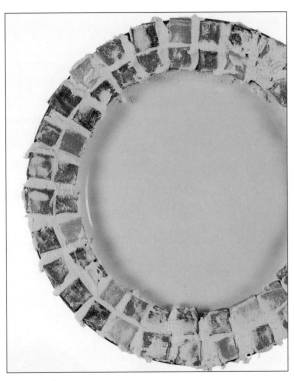

4 When the grout has set use the spatula to fill in with more grout between the tiles. Check that it finishes neatly at the edges and allow it 24 hours to dry.

5 You will now need a cloth to wipe off any excess grout and polish up the tiles. When the tiles look clean apply a layer of varnish to give them a shine. Let's hope the birds enjoy their new bird bath!

LEAVES, PEBBLES AND MOSS
Plate Gardens

While away a rainy afternoon making a miniature garden. These realistic-looking gardens are laid out on dinner plates. You could create an imaginary garden or recreate a section of your own garden. Have a look around outside for plants and tiny flowers to use to decorate your plate garden. Make fences from lollysticks or twigs and use your imagination to help you create miniature copies of real life objects. Use tiny pebbles to make a garden path. See if you can find some miniature ornaments that will be the right scale for garden statues.

You will need:
Plate

Sand

Potting compost

Pebbles

Sticks and thread

Dried flowers and moss

Selection of leaves and flowers

Modelling clay

Salt

Scissors

Paper

1 Place a layer of sand on a plate and cover it with a layer of potting compost. Use small pebbles to lay a path. Make some beanpoles from twigs tied with thread and press them firmly into the earth. Use some moss to create a hedge.

2 The garden is now ready for the vegetables to be 'planted'. A small leaved plant stem has been wound round the beanpoles, and a slightly larger leaved plant stem is laid on the earth. The carrot leaves are made from maidenhair fern with clay models of vegetables and garden tools laid amongst the leaves.

3 The washing is drying in a corner of this sweet little flower garden. Begin with a layer of sand on a plate and cover that with a thin layer of potting compost. Use some checked paper to make the path and two long twigs tied with a piece of string to make the washing line. A piece of paper is cut to make the white picket fence. Now cut some paper clothes to hang on the line.

4 The washing is hung on the line and the garden in now full of flowers and plants. Use moss as plants and some dried flowers pressed into the earth.

5 This winter scene is very effective. Place a layer of sand on the plate and make a snowman from modelling clay. Plant a few moss bushes and press some twigs into the sand. When your model is arranged pour salt over everything to create a snowscene.

RECYCLED MILK CARTONS
Bird Feeders

Whether you live in the town or the country there will be wild birds about. You can easily attract the birds to your garden or windowsill by placing some wild bird seed in a small bird feeder where cats cannot get to it. The birds will enjoy a good feed and you will learn to recognize the different species. The bird feeder is made from an empty milk carton. If you hang it near a window you can keep an eye on the birds while you are out of sight, indoors. You might also want to thread some peanuts on a string and hang them out for the birds.

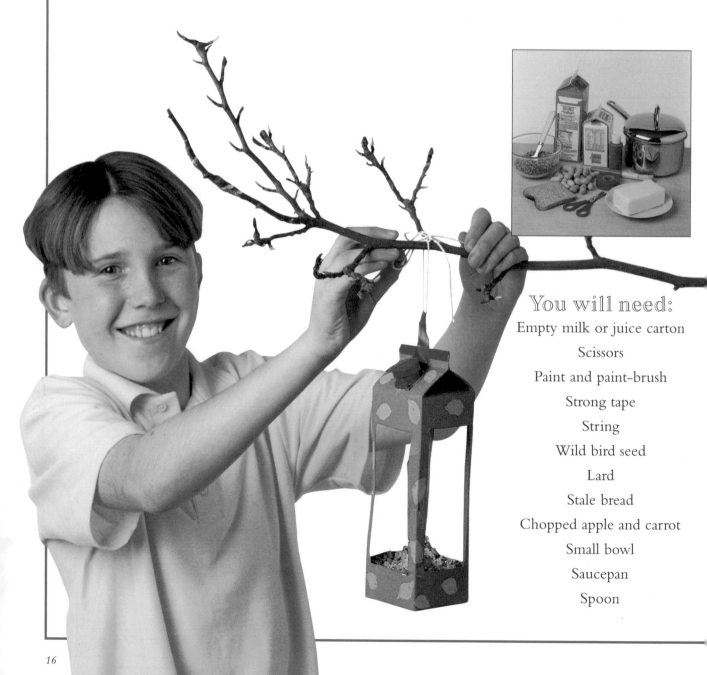

You will need:

Empty milk or juice carton

Scissors

Paint and paint-brush

Strong tape

String

Wild bird seed

Lard

Stale bread

Chopped apple and carrot

Small bowl

Saucepan

Spoon

1 Making this bird feeder is a good way to recycle a milk or juice carton. Cut away most of the sides of the carton leaving space at the base to hold the bird seed.

2 Once you have got the shape of the bird feeder right you can paint it. Choose a colour that will blend in with the surroundings and not frighten off the birds.

3 When the paint is dry you can decorate the bird feeder. Attach a piece of strong tape in a loop to the top of the feeder and fill the base with some wild bird seed.

4 Hang your bird feeder in a place, safe from the reach of cats. Thread some peanuts on a piece of string and hang that up alongside the feeder.

5 To make a bird seed ball you will need a saucepan and some lard, available from a supermarket. Melt the lard in a saucepan over a low heat (you may need an adult to help you with this). Collect the rest of your ingredients together. You can use old bread and wild bird seed and could always add some chopped carrot, assorted nuts or apple to the mixture.

6 Break a slice of bread into small pieces and place them in a bowl; pour over the melted lard. Add the wild bird seed and mix well together. As the mixture cools you will be able to form it into a ball. Push a piece of string into the centre of the mixture. Once it has hardened you will be able to hang the ball up with the string, alongside your bird feeder.

FLOWERS AND LEAVES
Pressed Flowers

Flower pressing was a popular activity among ladies in the nineteenth century. Nowadays flower pressing is regaining popularity as a hobby. If you have a garden it is easy to find flowers to press, although you should check with an adult before you pick any flowers. Pressing flowers dries them out, flattening them and leaving a little of the original colour. This creates a material you can use to decorate writing paper and greeting cards, and if you press enough flowers you could create a whole picture or cover a small box. Once you have pressed your flowers, store them flat between layers of tissue paper in a box in a dry, airy place to save their colour.

You will need:
Fresh picked flowers to press

Flower press or old book

Scissors

Glue

Items to decorate

When picking flowers to press make sure that they have no insects in them, and that the petals are perfect, not torn or brown.

Put the flowers in your flowerpress or in tissue between the pages of a thick book, as soon after picking as possible.

1 Pressing flowers is a wonderful hobby. Press the flowers flat in a flowerpress or use an old book. The flowers will need to be left in place for quite a few weeks before they are ready to use.

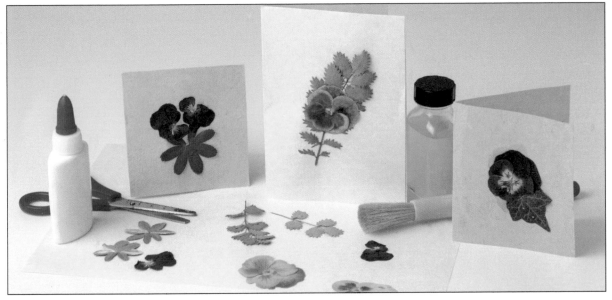

2 Pressed flowers can be used to decorate greeting cards. You can buy prepared cards to decorate or make your own from nice paper. Spend a little time trying out designs by laying different pressed flowers and leaves on the paper. When you are happy with your design use a little glue to attach the pressed flowers to the card. You may want to paint on a little varnish to give the picture a high gloss finish.

3 For a rose picture, press a whole rose carefully in your flowerpress. Leave it for a few weeks until most of the moisture has dried out. Choose a small frame and place the pressed rose in it. If you press lots of flowers you may have enough to cover a small box.

DRIED FLOWERS AND HERBS
Pot Pourri

To make your own pot pourri you will first need to gather a selection of fragrant petals and dry them in a warm, airy spot away from direct sunlight. Roses and lavender are both very sweet smelling and can easily be grown in a town or country garden. A handful of rose petals can be dried in a paper bag hung up in an airy spot and small bunches of lavender flowers can be hung up on a line to dry naturally in the air. Once you have dried your petals you will be able to mix up some pot pourri. You could place bowls of pot pourri around a room to make it smell of summer or make some lacy bags to contain small quantities of pot pourri to keep your drawers and clothes sweet smelling.

1 To dry rose petals you will need to place them in a warm airy spot away from direct sunlight. If you don't have the space to leave things out put a few petals in a paper bag and hang it up in an airy place. Choose some roses or other flowers which are sweet smelling. Check with an adult before you pick any flowers from the garden.

2 Besides petals you can dry orange and lemon peel, whole small flowers and some leaves. Spices can also be added to dried petals to enhance the perfume of the pot pourri. Cinnamon and mixed spice, cloves and nutmeg can all be put in pot pourri. If you don't have a flower garden to pick from, you may be able to purchase dried petals from your local wholefood shop. You could ask at the florist for any discarded flowers and buds.

3 One way of making good use of pot pourri is to tie it in lace or muslin bags to place in your drawers and cupboards. They will make your clothes smell sweet and some petals and leaves will discourage moths and other unwanted insects from living among your clothes. When, after some weeks the scent fades, fill the bags with newly made pot pourri.

Pot Pourri:

1 cup of fragrant dried rose petals and rosebuds

Half a cup of dried lavender petals

1 cinnamon stick, broken up

A large pinch of cloves

Dried orange peel, broken up

1 teaspoon of sea salt

Mix all the ingredients together in a bowl

You will need:
Dried rose petals and rosebuds
Dried lavender
Selection of dried fragrant leaves and petals
Bowl
Cinnamon sticks
Lace, muslin and ribbon
Needle and thread

Making Paper

Paper is made from recycled fibrous material, this could be newspaper, computer paper, sugar paper, mashed up pot pourri or leaves. You will need a small picture frame and an adult with a staple gun to help you make a paper making tray. The size of the picture frame will be the size of the sheet of paper you make, so bear that in mind when you choose your frame. Once you have mastered the art of paper making you can experiment with colours and textures. Try laying pressed flowers on the wet sheet of formed paper or using different coloured material. Food colouring can be used to colour paper to good effect.

You will need:

Staple gun

Fabric

Wooden picture frame

Torn up pieces of
sugar paper

Kitchen blender

Container

Newspaper

Kitchen cloths

Rolling pin

1 To make a paper making frame ask an
adult to staple a piece of fabric taut over
the back of a wooden picture frame.

2 Tear the paper up into small pieces and
place it in the blender. Cover well with
water. Blend until the paper is well
mashed. Ask an adult for help with the
electric blender.

3 Pour the well watered down paper pulp
into a container large enough to take the
paper making frame. You will need
enough pulp to half fill the container.

4 Lower the frame into the pulpy water and
swish it around getting a layer of paper
pulp into the frame. You may need to do
this a few times to get the pulp evenly
spread across the frame.

5 Lift the frame out of the water. Cover the
work surface with old newspaper and lay
a kitchen cloth on top of it.

6 In one movement tip the pulp out of the
frame. You may need to give the frame a
knock to get the pulp out. Place another
kitchen cloth on top of the paper and
press it down firmly.

7 Press evenly and firmly down on the
kitchen cloth using a rolling pin. This will
remove the excess water. You have now
made a sheet of paper.

8 In this picture there are two sheets of
hand made paper. You will need to practise to get the amounts of pulp right and
learn how to spread the pulp evenly
across the frame.

Oak-Galls, Fruits and Petals
Making Ink

People have been making ink since they could draw and write. Some of the oldest books in existence were written with ink made with oak-galls - try making some for yourself. Oak-galls are the swellings caused by gall wasp larvae burrowing into leaf buds. They are found on oak trees in autumn. Give them a good shake to ensure the insects have hatched and left home. You can also use coloured fruit juice as ink – blackcurrants, raspberries and mulberries all stain in shades of red, while daffodil petals make a yellow ink. If you wanted to be secretive, try writing a letter in lemon juice. Once the writing has dried, you can bring up the message by ironing the paper with a warm iron. The message will colour brown and you will be able to read it.

You will need:
Oak-galls, soft fruit or petals

Pestle and mortar

Jar

Water

Rusty nail

Piece of muslin

Lemon

Paper and pen

1 You will need to find some oak-galls to make this ink. Pick them in the autumn after the insects have flown. Two or three oak-galls will make a couple of tablespoons of ink. Put the oak-galls in a mortar and crush them using a pestle.

2 Place the crushed oak-galls in a jar and add a tablespoon of water for each one and one rusty nail. Leave the mixture to stand, uncovered. After an hour you will notice that the liquid begins to change colour. By the next day it should be quite dark and in a week it should be nearly black. Strain the ink through a piece of muslin and it is ready to use.

3 You can use dark coloured fruit juice as ink. Use a dipping pen to write with. Blackcurrants, raspberries and mulberries will give shades of red and you can make a yellow from daffodil petals. Try different vegetables – beetroot gives a good colour.

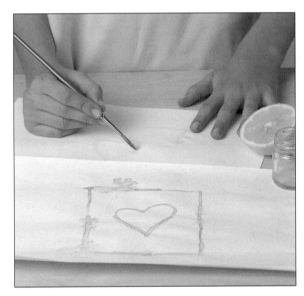

4 To make invisible ink you can use lemon juice. Squeeze the juice of half a lemon into a small container. Use a dipping pen or a thin paint-brush. Write your message on a sheet of paper and leave it to dry. To make the writing visible you will need to iron it, the writing will turn a brown colour with the heat from the iron. Ask an adult for help with the iron.

DRIED LAVENDER, MOSS AND ROSES
Dried Flowers

Drying flowers is a great hobby. Pick the flowers in summer and hang them up in an warm, dry and airy place. To prepare them for drying, remove any leaves on the stem and tie them into small bunches or they will dry unevenly.

It will take up to three weeks for them to dry. You can use them in a vase or create permanent arrangements of flowers in interesting containers. Dried flowers can also be used to decorate picture frames or make table settings for special occasions.

You will need:
Florist's foam

Knife

Terracotta pot

A selection of dried flowers

Glue

Scissors

A picture frame

1 Cut the florist's foam to fit. Place it in the flowerpot and press it down well.

2 Place a row of dried lavender bunches around the edge of the pot, pressing them into the foam.

3 Glue an edging of dried moss around the lavender on the edge of the pot. Using scissors, trim off any long or uneven pieces of moss.

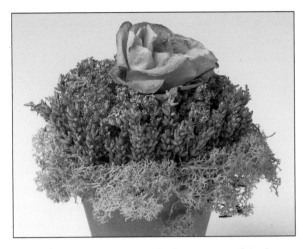

4 Use a little glue and place some dried flowers and a dried rose in the centre.

5 To make this dried flower picture frame you will need a cardboard frame, some dried moss and rosebuds. Begin by gluing the moss around the edge of the oval cut-out. Glue on the rosebuds and leave to dry. A picture frame would make an attractive gift. Offer it with a picture of you in the frame!

Bottle Gardens

Create a miniature oasis in a bottle. All you need to start a bottle garden is a large, empty sweet jar and some potting compost. Choose plants which will stay quite small; ask for assistance at your local garden centre or florist. Some garden centres have bottle garden departments where they sell small plants suitable for this enclosed, small environment. Bottle gardens should never have the sun shining directly onto them (they would get too hot), but they do need to be in a light situation. Keep the soil moist. You may not need to water often if the lid is kept firmly on. Feed your bottle garden every two weeks during the summer. Decorate it using glass paints and outliners. Choose a gold outliner for a stylish pattern or use black outliner and coloured paint to create a stained glass effect on the exterior of the bottle.

You will need:

Sticks

Old spoon

Wire

Kitchen sponge

Cotton wool

A large empty sweet jar

Pebbles or gravel

Suitable potting compost

Suitable plants

Glass paints outliner

Glass paint

1 Begin by making some suitable bottle garden tools. For a digging tool, use an old spoon attached with wire to a long stick. Use a piece of kitchen sponge wired onto a stick to press the earth down when you are planting. Lastly, you will need a cleaning tool. For this use a piece of cotton wool wired onto a stick (you may need a few of these to tidy up the bottle garden once it is planted).

2 Place a thin layer of pebbles or gravel in the base of the bottle. This will provide drainage for the bottle garden plants.

3 Cover the pebbles with a thick layer of potting compost. Press the compost down gently using your sponge tool.

4 Use the digging tool to place individual plants in position. Press the compost down firmly around the plants, taking care not to damage their roots.

5 Use the cotton wool tool to clean up the sides of the bottle garden. Wipe away any smears or pieces of compost that have stuck to the sides of the jar.

6 Your bottle garden is now ready to decorate. Choose a simple pattern and mark it out with the outliner. The stained glass effect will resemble a mini-conservatory.

When choosing plants for your bottle garden choose low growing varieties. Keep the compost moist but do not overwater. Feed your bottle garden every two weeks in the growing season.

SALT AND FLOUR DOUGH
Fragrant Wall Plaque

Keep your room sweet smelling with a fragrant wall plaque. Made from salt and flour dough the shapes are cut using biscuit cutters. Add a few drops of essential oil to give them a nice aromatic smell. Hang your plaques on the bedroom wall or in a wardrobe and they will smell sweet for a few months. You can always add more drops of oil when the perfume fades.

1 To make the salt and flour dough place the flour, salt and water in a large bowl. Stir the mixture with a wooden spoon until it forms a dough. Remove from the bowl and knead for 5 minutes. When smooth, roll out the dough on a floured surface and cut out shapes with the biscuit cutters. Place them on a greased baking sheet. Use the end of a straw to poke a hole in each shape (this is where the ribbon hanger threads through later). Bake the shapes in the oven at 130°C, 266°F, gas mark 1-2 for 4 hours or until completely dry.

2 When the shapes are dry and cool they are ready for painting on both sides. Leave a centimetre square area unpainted. This is where you put 2 or 3 drops of the essential oil to give the plaque its fragrance. When the paint is dry push a length of ribbon through the hole. Knot the ribbon and hang the plaque in the wardrobe or on the wall.

You will need:
2 cups flour
1 cup salt
1 cup of water
Large bowl
Wooden spoon
Rolling pin
A little spare flour
Biscuit cutters
Baking tray
Paint
Paint-brush
Acrylic paint
Straw
Sweet smelling essential oil
(such as Lavender or Neroli)

In the Kitchen

VEG, MEAT AND FISH
Burgers

Follow our easy recipes for burgers which are quick to prepare and delicious to eat. Make them from minced meat, cooked beans, tofu or fish. There is a recipe to suit every taste. For a professional look serve your burgers with a garnish such as a slice of lemon, cress or sliced tomato and lettuce.

You will need:
Ingredients

Bowl

Potato masher

Wooden spoon

Frying pan

Plates and cutlery to serve

Bean Burgers:
1 can of black-eyed beans

1 small chopped onion, fried

1 teaspoon mixed herbs

1 egg

1 cup of wholemeal breadcrumbs

Flour to roll the finished burgers in

A little oil for frying

Tofu Burgers:
250g block of tofu, chopped

1 small chopped onion, fried

2 teaspoons fresh or dried parsley

1 cup wholemeal breadcrumbs

2 teaspoons soya sauce

Sesame seeds to roll finished burgers in

A little oil for frying

Fish burgers:
155g tin pilchards in tomato sauce

1 cup wholemeal breadcrumbs

1 small chopped onion, fried

1 teaspoon mixed herbs

Flour to roll the finished burgers in

A little oil for frying

Lamb burgers:
250g minced lamb

1 teaspoon mixed herbs

salt and pepper to taste

1 egg

half a cup of whole-meal breadcrumbs

Flour to roll the finished burgers in

A little oil for frying

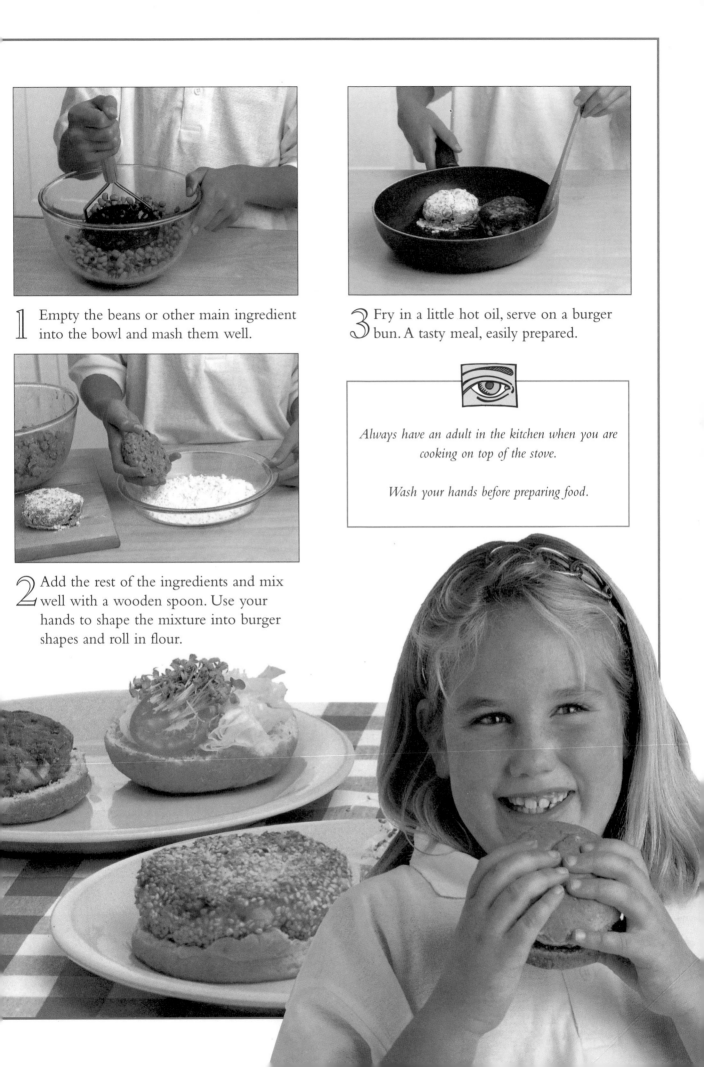

1 Empty the beans or other main ingredient into the bowl and mash them well.

2 Add the rest of the ingredients and mix well with a wooden spoon. Use your hands to shape the mixture into burger shapes and roll in flour.

3 Fry in a little hot oil, serve on a burger bun. A tasty meal, easily prepared.

Always have an adult in the kitchen when you are cooking on top of the stove.

Wash your hands before preparing food.

PEPPERMINT AND CHOCOLATE
Sweets

You will need:

12 tablespoons of icing sugar

1 egg-white

Peppermint flavouring

Green food colouring

Wooden spoon

Bowl

Knife and board

Plain chocolate

Small bowl

Foil

Tray

Glacé cherries

Home-made sweets are fun to make and delicious to eat! Try your hand at chocolate-dipped peppermints or cherries. The fruit is made from marzipan and painted with food colouring. You may find that making them takes a little practice, but once you have mastered the art you could make a bowl of miniature marzipan fruit. Have a look at some real fruit for inspiration. Fresh fruit can also be dipped into chocolate – try it with some orange segments.

1 Place the icing sugar, egg-white, 4 drops peppermint flavouring, 12 drops green colouring into a bowl and mix well. You may need to add a little more icing sugar. Knead the mixture for a few minutes until it forms a smooth ball.

2 Form the mixture into a sausage shape and slice into discs. Use your hands to shape the discs into round sweet shapes and place on a board to dry.

3 Ask an adult to melt the chocolate in a small bowl. Dip the dry peppermints into the melted chocolate until they are half covered. Place the chocolate dipped peppermints on a foil-covered tray to set.

4 To make chocolate-dipped cherries, first wash the syrup off the glacé cherries. Pat them dry with kitchen towel and use a cocktail stick to dip them into the melted chocolate. Decorate the dipped cherries with a small piece of cherry.

Always wash your hands before you handle food.

Remember to tidy up as you go along.

Egg Cups

Boiled eggs for breakfast will never be the same again with one of these fun egg cups. They are made from air-hardening clay. Make a Humpty Dumpty egg cup for a young brother or sister, or choose a more stylish crown or simple shape painted to match your breakfast plates. Make a set of egg cups, one for each member of the family, decorated to suit their hobbies or interests.

You will need:

A block of air hardening clay

Clay modelling tool

Tray to stand the egg cup on while it is drying

Acrylic paints

Paint-brush

Varnish

1 Begin by shaping a block of clay to be the wall for Humpty to sit on.

3 When the model is completely dry, you can decorate it. Paint one colour at a time allowing each shade to dry.

2 Make the legs and arms from sausage shapes and use an egg to gauge the size of the cup. Once you have made your model, leave it to dry for 24 hours.

4 Varnish the egg cup when the paint is completely dry.

Before you begin, cover your work surface with newspaper or a plastic cloth — working with clay can be a messy business. It is a good idea to work on a tray which will enable you to carry your finished item to a safe place to dry.

If you cannot get hold of air hardening clay, make Humpty from salt and flour dough: mix 2 cups of plain flour and 1 cup of fine salt, add 1 cup of water and mix well. Knead for 5 minutes, then the dough will be ready for use.

Toast Racks

Brighten up the breakfast table with one of these easy to make toast racks. They are made from recycled grocery boxes and torn up strips of newspaper. Before you begin have a look around the kitchen and choose a colour and style that will match.

Some toast racks have space for butter pats and jam while others only have room for toast. When you have made one of the simple shapes you could try something a little different. A nicely made toast rack would make a good gift for a friend or neighbour.

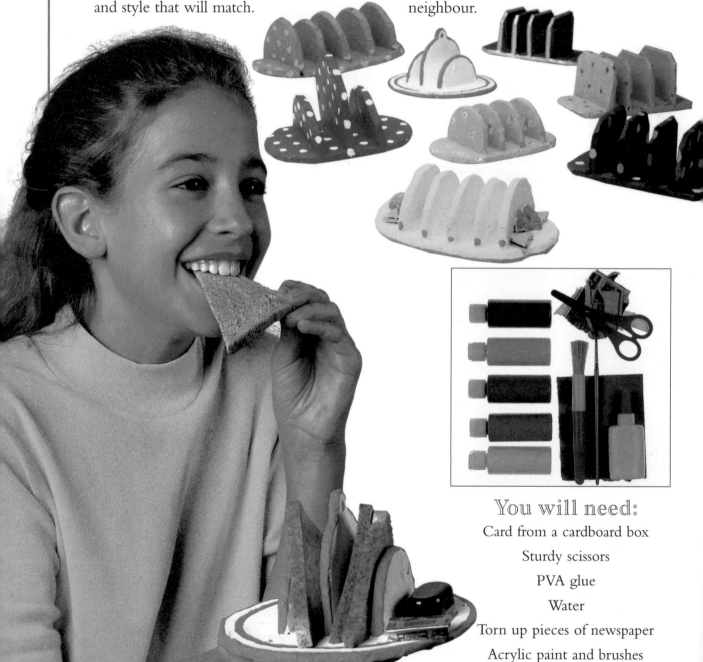

You will need:
Card from a cardboard box

Sturdy scissors

PVA glue

Water

Torn up pieces of newspaper

Acrylic paint and brushes

1 Use card from a grocery box to cut out an oval-shaped base and four racks. You will need a pair of sturdy scissors.

4 Mix an equal quantity of PVA (white) glue with water. Glue small torn pieces of newspaper all over your model.

2 Use the blade of the scissors to score the card then tear out slots for the racks. Remember to leave enough space for the slices of toast between the racks.

5 When the toast rack is completely dry it is ready to decorate. Use acrylic paint and a design that matches the shape of your toast rack.

3 Glue the racks into place and set aside until the glue has dried.

Remember to protect your work surface with newspaper or a vinyl cloth.

If you don't have any glue, get an adult to help you make some. Mix two cups of water and one cup of flour in a saucepan and cook it gently, stirring all the time, until it is thick, creamy and sticky.

Fabric Printing

Decorate a traycloth or table napkins with apple or carrot prints. The prints are made using real fruit and vegetables cut in half. Green peppers make good prints too. Fabric paints come in plenty of colours and are easy to use – follow the directions written on the container. Always try your design out on a piece of scrap paper before you print on the fabric to test out how much fabric paint you need.

Protect your worksurface with newspaper before you begin. Keep some kitchen towel handy in case of spills.

If you cannot get hold of fabric paint, try using acrylic paint. You will not be able to wash the cloth but it will make a great wall hanging for the kitchen.

You will need:

Vegetables

Knife

Sponge

Fabric paint

Squares of fabric

Biscuit cutters

Kitchen towel

1 Cut a carrot in half. Use a sponge to spread a little fabric paint onto the carrot half. Gently press it down onto the fabric. Only press once and do not move it about when you press. Print a row of carrots on the cloth. Leave the printed cloth in a safe place to dry. Follow the directions that come with the fabric paint to set the dye.

2 Cut a potato in half. Press the biscuit cutter firmly into the flesh of the potato. Use a knife to carefully cut away the excess potato. Remove the biscuit cutter and you have a stamp ready for printing. Pat the stamp dry with some kitchen towel. Use a sponge to apply the fabric paint to the potato cut and print your pattern.

3 Halved apples printed on this green table mat look jolly. You will need to pat the cut surface dry with a piece of kitchen towel. Use the sponge to apply red fabric paint to the apple surface and press firmly down onto the green table mats.

GLASS AND PAINT

Glass Painting

Glass painting is a great hobby and a good way of recycling empty jam jars and bottles or personalising glasses to give away as gifts or use in the home. Glass paints also work well on plastic containers, so collect a few large plastic containers and decorate them for use in the kitchen, for storing dried pasta or beans. Glass paints come in a wide variety of colours and are easy to use. Experiment with simple designs at first. Always try out your ideas on paper before painting on glass. If you make a mistake on the glass wipe the paint off quickly and start again.

1. Before you begin wash and dry the glass. Use the black outliner to mark up the pattern. Be sure there are no gaps for the glass paint to escape through. When the black outliner is completely dry use a dry brush to dip into the glass paint. Wash the brush well between colours and dry it before dipping it into the next colour.

2. Use the gold outliner on its own for this stylish look. Think about what will be in the container when deciding on colour and design.

3. Save tiny jars to decorate and fill with jam.

You will need:

Selection of glasses, jars and bottles

Outliners in black, gold and silver

Paint-brush

Water-soluble glass paints

Kitchen towel for spills

Remember to protect your work surface with newspaper before you begin.

Always make sure the glasses and jars are washed and dried with a clean cloth before you begin to decorate them.

Fridge Magnets

Liven up the fridge with a bright blue teapot or a friendly teddy bear fridge magnet. These fridge magnets are made from oven bake clay, which comes in a wide range of colours.

Fruit and vegetable magnets look good in the kitchen, and a bright red apple containing a friendly little worm, will bring a smile to everyone's face when at the fridge door.

Follow the manufacturer's directions when baking the clay.

Always have an adult present when using the cooker.

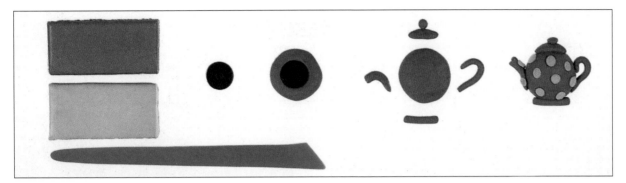

1 Before you begin, make sure your hands are spotlessly clean as dirt transfers to the clay very quickly and can't be removed.

Knead the clay in your hand until it is soft enough to use. Shape the teapot following the steps in the picture.

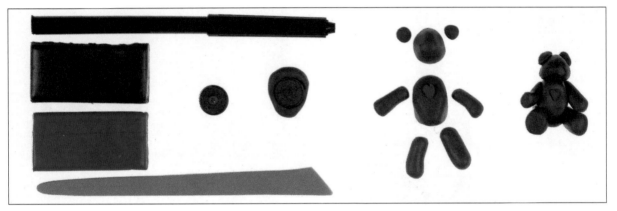

2 The bear is made from dark brown clay. Make his arms and legs from short sausage shapes. Give him a bright red nose, a bow

tie or even a coloured hat! If the magnet doesn't stick, glue it on once your model is out of the oven and cooled down.

You will need:
Oven bake clay in a variety of colours

Knife

Clean surface on which to roll your clay

Small rolling pin or a suitable pen lid

Baking tray covered with foil

Magnets

Glue

3 This carrot magnet is made from yellow and red clay mixed to give a good orange carroty colour. Make the stalk from short rolls of green clay, squashed together.

Frames

Frame a special photograph in one of these pretty frames. They are made out of card from a grocery box and covered with aluminium foil. Choose a simple shape and expect a few discards while you master the method. Simple patterns are best to decorate the frames: flowers, hearts or stars for example. Have a look around the kitchen and you may find coloured foil you could recycle. The gold foil frame is made with recycled margarine tub foil! Try sprucing up an old picture frame by covering it with foil.

You will need:

Thick card (from a grocery box)

Ruler

Strong scissors

Foil

Glue

Pencil and ball point pen

Remember foil is made from metal and can be sharp – take care.

1 Use a photograph to measure how large the frame should be. Cut out the foil shape a few centimetres larger than the card frame.

4 Attach the frame to the backing with glue on three sides, leaving an opening to slip in the photograph.

2 Spread the card frame with glue and making sure there is no glue on your fingers, gently press the foil over the frame. Tuck the edges in well, smoothing the foil carefully.

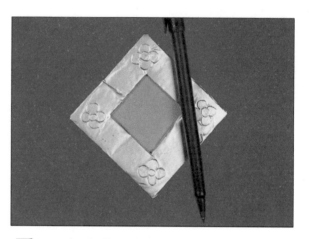

5 Use the ball point pen to mark the design onto the frame.

3 Cover the backing of the frame with foil.

PLAIN AND CHOCOLATE
Biscuits

For a special treat, home-made biscuits decorated with icing, silver balls cherries and sprinkles, will brighten up your tea time. Try both recipes (plain and chocolate), cut out in a variety of shapes with a mixture of patterns and designs, to create a colourful plateful of delicious biscuits. A few home-made biscuits in a decorative box or bag makes an ideal gift for parents or neighbours.

1   Use a wooden spoon to mix the flour, margarine (or butter), vanilla essence, sugar and baking powder until it looks like breadcrumbs. Add the egg and mix with a wooden spoon until it forms a dough.

2   Sprinkle a little flour onto the work surface and roll out the dough with a rolling pin. Do not press too hard. Dip the cutters in flour before cutting out a selection of shapes.

3   Place the biscuits on a greased baking tray. Bake for 15 minutes at 180°C, 350°F, gas mark 4. Allow to cool and decorate with icing, silver balls, cherries and sprinkles.

Ingredients

250g plain flour

125g margarine or butter

75g castor sugar

1 teaspoon baking powder

1 egg

For plain biscuits add:

1 teaspoon vanilla essence

For chocolate biscuits add:

25g cocoa powder

You will need:

Wooden spoon

Bowl

Biscuit cutters

Biscuit decorations

Ask an adult to help when using the cooker.

ICE CREAM
Sundaes

Have an ice cream sundae party for your friends. You will need a selection of ice creams, fresh fruit, custard, cream, jellies and decorative sprinkles. Try the home-made strawberry ice cream recipe, it is quick and easy to make. Fruit yoghurts can also be frozen and make tasty ice cream.

Always have an adult present when using sparklers or other fireworks.

Banana and chocolate ice cream sundae

Put one layer at a time into the glass. Start with some sliced banana, then add a spoonful of cold custard. Sprinkle on some chocolate flakes, then a small scoop of vanilla ice cream and decorate with heaps of whipped cream.

Strawberry trifle

Begin with a layer of crushed trifle biscuits. Mix 2 teaspoons of strawberry jam with 2 teaspoons of warm water and pour over the biscuits. Follow with custard then some chopped strawberries and jelly.
Finally decorate with whipped cream and a whole strawberry.

Sparkling ice cream sundae

Place a small tin of evaporated milk in the fridge for 2 hours. Pour the milk into a bowl and use a whisk to whip it until it is light and fluffy. Mix in the strawberries and syrup. Pour the mixture into a freezer-proof dish and freeze until solid. Serve it with a dazzling sparkler.

Miniature Teatime

Teatime in the doll's house will go with a swing when you have made this tiny teaset and strawberry cream sponge. They are made from oven hardening clay and baked in the oven. If you don't have any oven hardening clay to hand you might want to use plasticene.

1 To make the miniature strawberry sponge cake begin with the plate. Use a flattened ball of red clay to make this. Next make two buff layers and two white layers and assemble the cake. Make some tiny strawberry shapes from red clay and place them carefully on top of the cake.

You will need:

Oven hardening clay
White paint
Paint-brush
Baking tray
Yellow paper
Felt tip pen

2 Make the teapot and cups with matching saucers from red clay. Make a large ball of clay for the teapot. Make smaller balls for the tea cups and press in your finger to form the cup shape. To make the handles and spout roll out thin sausage shapes and press them into position. Add a tiny ball of clay to make a teapot lid. To make the saucers flatten out balls of clay with your hand. Place the cake and crockery on a baking tray and bake according to the manufacturer's instructions. When the pieces are hardened, paint tiny white spots on the cups, saucers and the teapot. Decorate a piece of yellow paper with felt tip pens and lay out your miniature tea.

Indoor Crafts

TISSUE AND WIRE
Paper Flowers

Surprise a friend with a bunch of scarlet poppies and fantasy flowers. They are made from tissue paper and florist's wire. The poppies are made up of individual petals and look quite realistic with their black-fringed stamens. The fantasy flowers are easy to make from layers of different colours – let your imagination run riot and create a rainbow bouquet.

You will need:

Glue

Tissue paper in a variety of colours

Florist's wire

Green florist's tape

Scissors

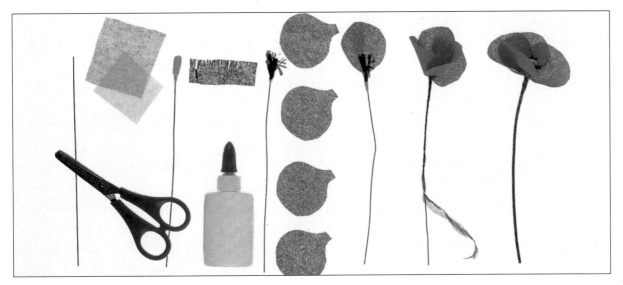

1 Glue a scrunched-up piece of tissue paper onto one end of a piece of wire, for the centre of the poppy. Now glue the square of green paper over the poppy centre. Roll the black-fringed piece around the centre of the flower to make the stamens. Glue on the petals one at a time. Bend them slightly so they look realistic. Finally, use the green tape to tidy up the base of the flower and cover the wire.

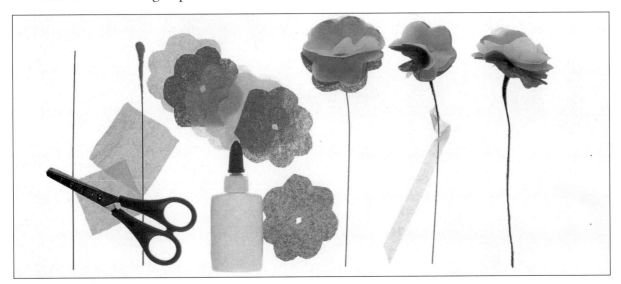

2 Fantasy flowers are made from layers of coloured flower shapes. Begin by cutting the shape for the base or sepals of the flower. Layer three colours of tissue paper together, cut out a flower shape and then cut a small hole through the centre of the papers. Wind a small piece of paper around a wire to make the flower centre. Now use glue to attach the green sepal shape and the coloured flowers. Finally use the green tape to tidy up the base of the flower and cover the wire.

Making paper flowers takes practise. Don't expect the first one to come out perfectly, so keep trying. When you get a good shape make a bunch.

Beads

Turn ethnic-looking beads made from coloured felt into great chokers, bracelets and pendants. The beads are made from layers of felt glued or tied together. They are threaded on embroidery silk. Make a selection of colours and shapes and combine them with wooden beads to make an exotic necklace.

You will need:

Felt squares (from a craft shop)

Scissors

Fabric glue

Elastic band

Needle and coloured thread

Small quantity of stuffing

Ribbon

1 Cut three squares of coloured felt, each slightly smaller than the other. Layer them, using a little glue to hold them in place. Now roll them tightly in a sausage shape and hold in place with glue. You may need to wind a little thread around them or hold them in place with an elastic band. The glue will need to dry thoroughly. When the glue has set, use scissors to cut the sausage into beads.

2 You will need two squares of coloured felt. Cut out a heart shape from each colour, with one heart slightly smaller than the other. Place a little stuffing between the layers and sew them together with coloured thread. Make a ribbon loop at the top of the heart for threading.

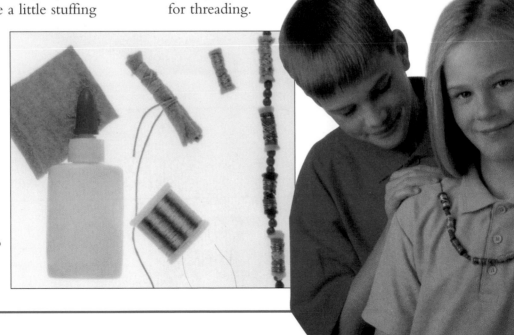

3 Roll up a small square of felt. Hold the roll in place with glue. Wind coloured thread around the sausage-shaped felt pieces to make decorative bands.

Friendship Bracelets

Friendship bracelets are easier to make than you think, they just take a little time to practise. Choose several threads in strong or pastel colour combinations. Find a corner to settle down on your own where you can work without interruption and in time you will master the art and make a braid to wear and one to give to a special friend.

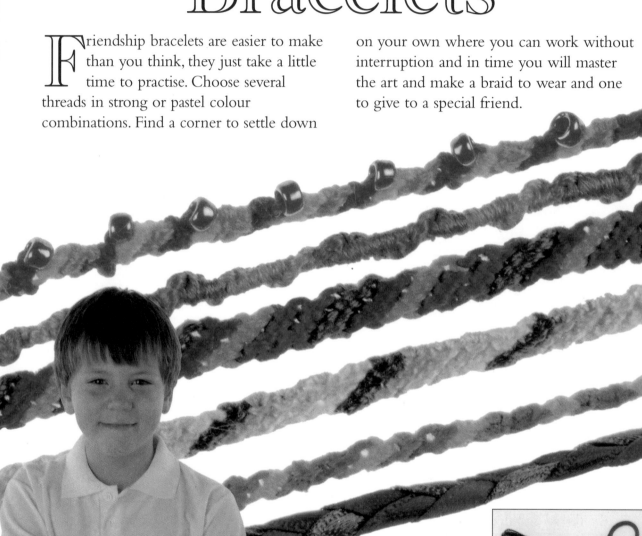

You will need:
Cork board or work surface
Selection of coloured thread
Sticky tape or safety pins
Scissors

1 You will need three lengths of thread. Make a knot to hold the threads together and attach the knot end to the board or work surface with sticky tape or a safety pin.

5 To start row two, make knots from left to right, knot B twice onto C, then twice onto A. For the third row, knot C twice onto A, then twice onto B.

2 Hold thread B with your left hand. Take thread A around B and push it through the loop to make a knot and pull the thread.

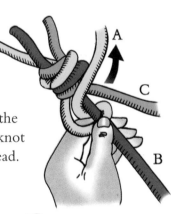

6 Keep knotting the threads in rows until you have made a braid long enough to go round your wrist. Tie a firm knot to hold the loose ends in place.

3 Repeat this action. You should have two knots on thread B.

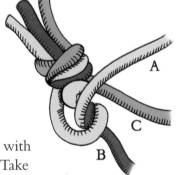

7 Your friendship bracelet is now complete – make a double knot at each end and trim away any excess thread.

4 Hold thread C with your left hand. Take thread A around C and through the loop to make a knot, pull the thread and then do it again. You should now have two knots on thread C. Thread A is now on the righthand side and you have completed the first row.

Remember to protect your work surface with newspaper or a vinyl cloth.

To make a wider braid use four, five or six threads. Make the braid as described above, knotting each thread twice, from left to right.

Brooches

se oven bake clay to make these cheeky brooches. Glitter-spangled stars, leaping dolphins, tiny toadstools or a fat pink pig – these will all look great on a felt beret or a coat lapel. The glitter star is made from coloured clay with the glitter glued on after baking. A coat of varnish gives a good finish.

1 To make this pink pig brooch start with a disc of pink clay to make the face. The nose is made from a small cylinder shape. Use the modelling tool or a cocktail stick to mark nostrils on the nose. The ears are made from flattened tear drop shapes flapping over the face. Make two little black eyes and when all the parts are assembled, place your pig brooch on an oven tray, ready for baking.

2 To make a cluster of toadstools, begin by making three stalks, one large and two small, out of yellow clay. Squash them gently together. Now make the caps from red clay and press them carefully onto the stalks. Decorate the caps with tiny yellow dots and your toadstool brooch is now ready for baking. After baking, when the clay has cooled, varnish the shapes. With an adult's help, glue on the brooch backs.

You will need:

Oven bake clay in a variety of colours

Modelling tool

Oven tray

Varnish

Brooch backs

Suitable glue

When using oven bake clay you will need to soften the clay first by moulding it between your fingers.

Follow the manufacturer's directions when baking the clay.

Always have an adult present when using the cooker.

Ask an adult for help when attaching the fastener to the brooch as you will need to use a strong glue.

Mobiles

Recycle milk and juice containers and turn them into colourful mobiles. The sleepy sheep would look good above your bed and the stars and flowers could hang in a sunny window. The mobiles are painted using water-soluble glass paints and outliners. If you don't have those to hand you can use coloured, permanent markers instead to create a similar effect.

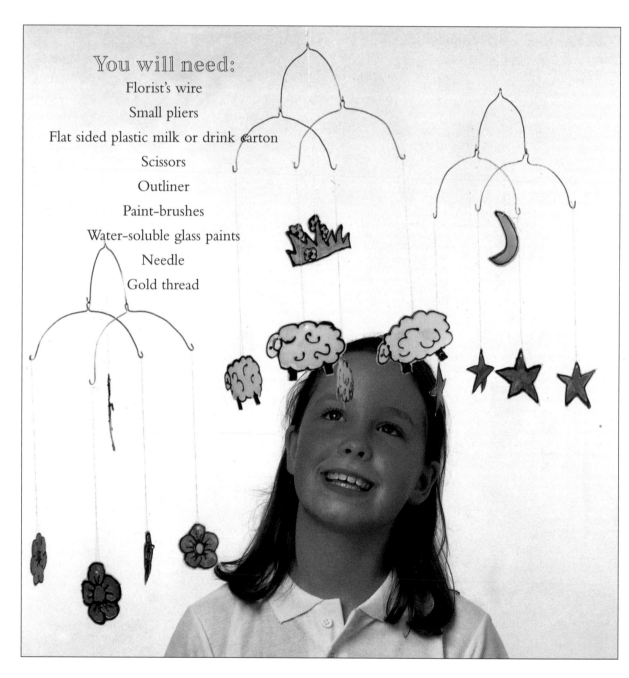

You will need:

Florist's wire

Small pliers

Flat sided plastic milk or drink carton

Scissors

Outliner

Paint-brushes

Water-soluble glass paints

Needle

Gold thread

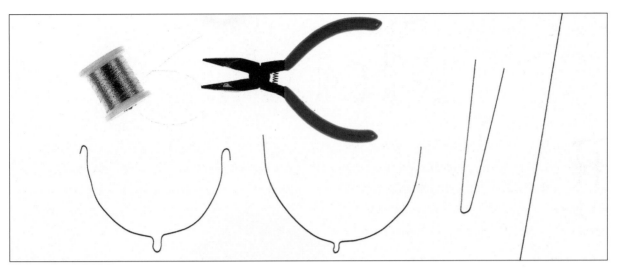

1 Florist's wire is easy to bend, start with a 20cm length. Begin by folding it in half. Then use the pliers to shape the mobile hanger and hooks. You will need three hangers for each mobile and each hanger should be exactly the same shape and size.

2 Use the scissors to cut the plastic container into suitable shapes for decoration. Wash the shapes and dry with a clean cloth. Outline the design and when the outliner is hard use a dry brush and glass paint to colour the shape.

3 Assemble the mobile by making a hole with the needle through the shapes and threading the gold thread through. Hang up the shapes and your mobile is complete.

Letter Rack

K eep your mail in check with these bright red tulips! The letter rack is made by slotting together thick coloured card shapes. Once you have mastered the technique you will be able to create your own designs, such as these flower patterns or maybe have a go at the ship at sea. The ship is a little more detailed, with the design cut from coloured paper.

1 Draw the design on thick, coloured card. The green bases will need to be cut straight to stand level on the table. The flowerheads are cut from coloured paper. Cut all the pieces out.

3 Glue on the flower heads and your letter rack is ready to hold the mail.

2 Colour the plain side of the card with crayons. Slot the letter rack together. You may need to make a rough one first to get the shape and slots right.

The letter rack can be made of card cut from a cereal packet or from a grocery box. You may need to cover the pieces of card with a layer of papier mâché to make them more sturdy and create a good surface to paint or colour.

You will need:
Thick coloured card

Scissors

Coloured paper

Crayons

Glue

Mirror Painting

Mirror, mirror on the wall who is the fairest of us all? Paint one of these pretty designs on a mirror tile to put up on the bathroom wall. The tiles are painted with glass paint which is available in a wide selection of colours and is very easy to use. The outliner divides the colours and comes in tubes that you use like a ball point pen, squeezing the colour gently onto the mirror.

You will need:
Mirror tiles or handbag mirrors

Glass paint outliners

Paper towel to mop up spills

Paint-brushes

Water-soluble glass paints

1 Use the outliner as if it were a pen, squeezing gently to allow a steady stream of the thick liquid onto the glass. Keep your paper towels handy in case of spills.

2 When the outliner is completely hard you can paint in the colour. Use a dry brush to dip into one colour at a time and wash and dry the brush well between colours.

Teddy Bears

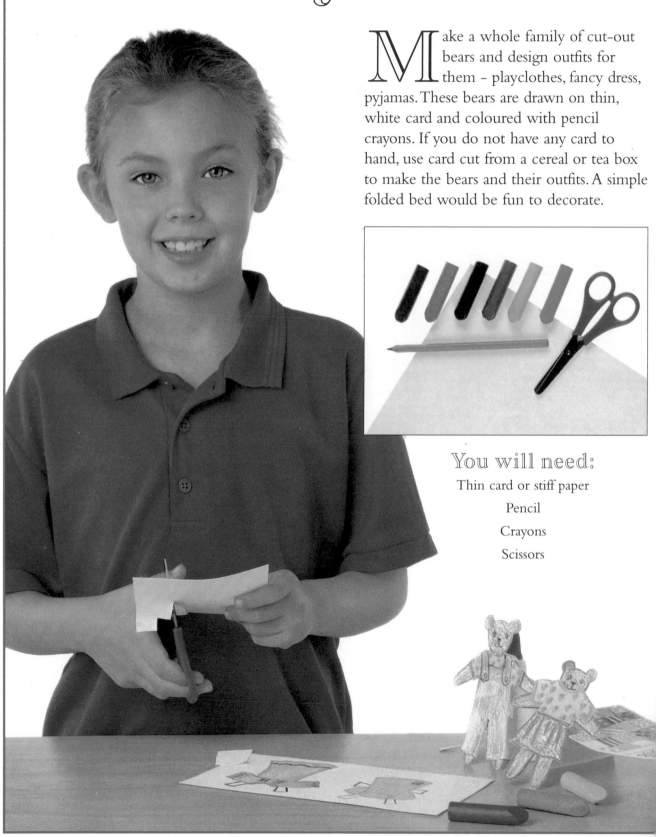

Make a whole family of cut-out bears and design outfits for them - playclothes, fancy dress, pyjamas. These bears are drawn on thin, white card and coloured with pencil crayons. If you do not have any card to hand, use card cut from a cereal or tea box to make the bears and their outfits. A simple folded bed would be fun to decorate.

You will need:

Thin card or stiff paper

Pencil

Crayons

Scissors

1 Draw a teddy bear onto thin card. Give it a face and colour it in using bright crayon colours. Cut it out. Make several members of a teddy bear family to dress.

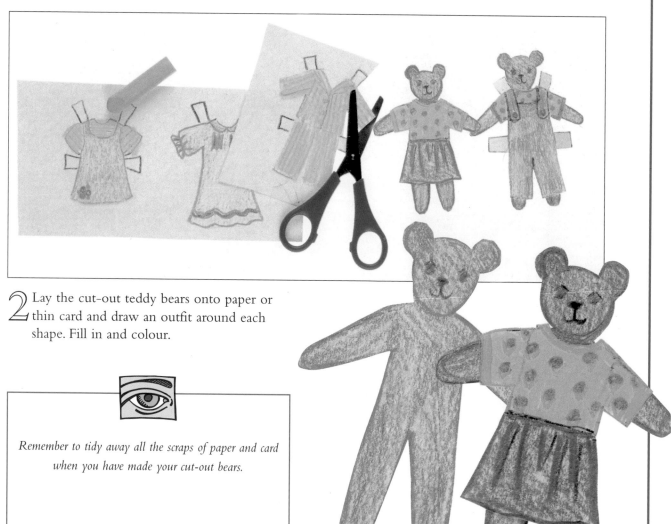

2 Lay the cut-out teddy bears onto paper or thin card and draw an outfit around each shape. Fill in and colour.

Remember to tidy away all the scraps of paper and card when you have made your cut-out bears.

Miniature Farm

This miniature farm can be made in an afternoon and could provide endless pleasure for a younger brother or sister. Stand it on a sunny windowsill to create a pretty country scene. Make a storage box for the farm from a matchbox covered with coloured paper and decorated in farmyard-style.

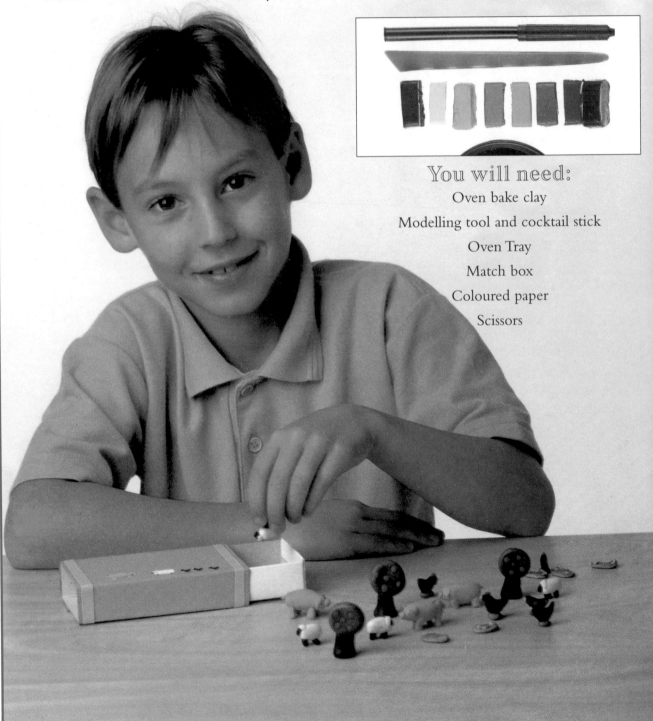

You will need:
Oven bake clay

Modelling tool and cocktail stick

Oven Tray

Match box

Coloured paper

Scissors

1 Begin by softening the white clay. Make the body first, then flatten a strip and fold it over the body as the ears. Now soften a small piece of black clay, and roll it into a sausage shape. Use the modelling tool to cut the legs and face.

2 These colourful hens are made from a small ball of brown clay. Press the clay to shape the head and tail of the hen. Make a base from a ball of green clay. Pinch out tiny pieces of red and yellow clay for the beak and comb.

3 First soften the pink clay. Make a nice round sausage shape for the body. The pig's snout is made from a small flattened ball and its ears are made from flattened teardrop shapes. Roll out a smaller sausage shape and use the modelling tool to cut short legs. Roll out a thin tail and attach it firmly to the body.

To make some little patches of daisy-covered grass flatten an oval shape of green clay. Then make some small balls of yellow and green clay and use a cocktail stick or the tip of your modelling tool to lift them up and press them down onto the clay grass. When all your models are made, place them on a baking tray and harden them in the oven.

Follow the manufacturer's directions when baking the clay.

If you can't buy oven bake clay, you can use plasticine.

Scrunchies

Easy to make, you can have a scrunchy for every occasion. Sew them by hand in a running stitch or ask an adult to sew them for you, using a sewing machine. Thread them with elastic and decorate them imaginatively. Make scrunchies from ribbon, lace, velvet or dress fabric. A brightly coloured towelling scrunchy would be good for the seaside or swimming pool.

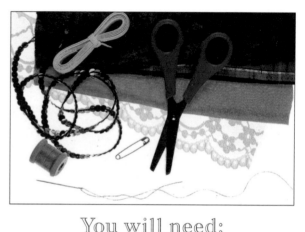

You will need:

Fabric and lace

Needle and thread or a sewing machine

Medium-sized safety pin

Half-centimetre wide elastic

Scissors

Sequins and glue

1 Lace: sew a centimetre-wide hem along one edge of the lace. Use the safety pin to thread the elastic through the seam. Tie the ends of the elastic into a knot and shape the scrunchy.

3 Tartan: this attractive scrunchy is made in the same way as the velvet scrunchy. Use matching thread to sew the seams.

2 Velvet: fold the fabric in half lengthways, with the wrong side out. Sew a seam. Turn the velvet tube the right way round by pulling one end through the other. Sew a channel in matching thread along one side and thread the elastic through.

4 Sequin: make this party time scrunchy in the same way as the tartan and velvet scrunchies. Decorate it with shiny sequins glued or sewn onto the fabric.

AIR HARDENING CLAY
Brilliant Beads

Rolling beads from clay is a good rainy day craft. These beads are made from air hardening clay and painted with bright colours. Use a fine paint-brush to paint on the tiny flowers or white spots. Maybe you could design a special pattern to go with a special outfit.

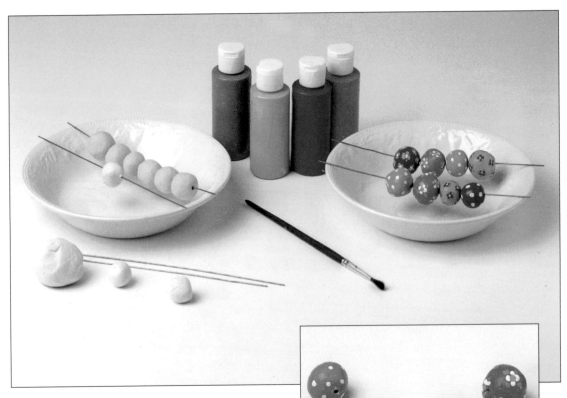

1 Make balls of clay in your chosen size (you might want to make small beads for a necklace or chunky beads for a bracelet). Push the wire through the middle of each ball wiggling it a bit to create a good sized hole. Lie the wired beads across the bowl and leave them in a dry airy spot to harden completely. Leave the beads on the wires while you paint and then varnish them. When you are happy with them, remove them from the wires and thread your home made beads as a necklace or bracelet.

You will need:
Air hardening clay
Wire
Bowl or box to lie the wired beads across while they dry
Paint-brush
Paint
Water soluble varnish
Thread

Cards and Wrappings

PAPER
Gift Boxes

Surprise your friends with one of these stylish hand made boxes. Make small boxes from paper or slightly larger boxes from thin card. A double layer of wrapping paper would make an attractive box. Use paper that suits the gift and make a box from flowery paper to hold packets of seeds or use red paper for a Valentine box. Plain paper can be decorated with stickers or coloured tape. Try decorating paper first with crayons or pencils. A set of boxes could be used to hold cake and party favours and you could personalize the boxes with your guests' names. Once you have mastered the method you will find the boxes quick and easy to make.

You will need:
Paper

Ruler

Scissors

Glue

1 Fold a rectangular piece of paper in half.

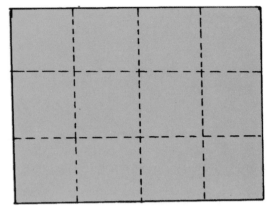

5 Now the creases should look like this.

2 Fold each half in on itself, so that both ends meet in the middle.

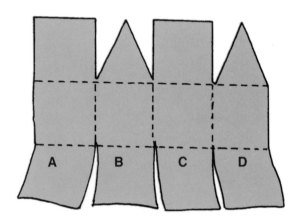

6 Cut along the crease lines and cut out the triangles as shown in the picture above.

3 With the paper opened out, you will see crease marks like this.

4 Now fold the paper into thirds in the opposite direction to your first folds.

7 Fold in and glue flap B onto flap A, flap C onto flap B and flap D onto flap C. Finally stick the open edge with sticky tape on the inside and make a hole at the top of both triangles for a ribbon.

Pop-up Cards

This pop-up card is simple to make and will brighten up someone's day. When placed on a windowsill or mantlepiece it will look as if a bunch of flowers is bursting out of the card. The cards are made and decorated with thin card. If you don't have any coloured thin card available, use card from a cereal packet and paint it in bright colours yourself.

You will need:

Coloured thin card

Scissors

Glue

Coloured paper

Felt tips pens

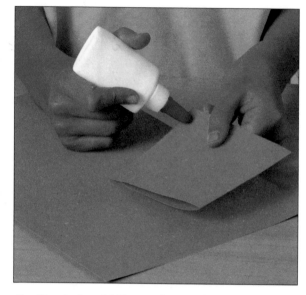

1 Begin by folding a sheet of thin card in half and then open it out. Cut out a small square of card and fold it in half. Fold a lip on the two edges, and glue these into the card to make the vase. Open and close the card to check the vase flattens when you close it.

2 Using green thin card, cut the stalks and leaves, use glue to attach these to the inside of the vase. Cut out some tulip-shaped flowers and glue them onto the stalks, making sure that they are hidden when the card is closed.

3 Cut small heart shapes to decorate the vase from red paper, folded over.

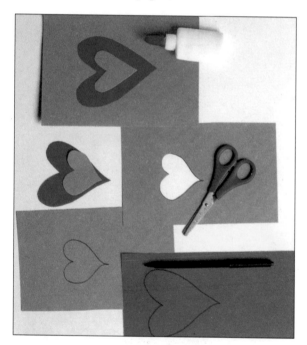

4 Now decorate the front of the card with a large red heart and a smaller blue heart, to match the rest of the design. Now you are ready to write your message on the card, using felt tip pens.

When trying out something for the first time, start by making a rough example out of scrap paper and card.

PAPER
Printed Cards

Spend a rainy afternoon making potato cuts to print with and you will be able to set up a production line and make a collection of cards or writing paper. The fish card is made with layers of different coloured paper, each slightly smaller than the other. Biscuit cutters come in lots of shapes and provide a quick way to make home made stamps. Use a small rabbit shape to decorate writing paper and envelopes. The bunch of carrots is made by first drawing the shape onto the potato half, then cutting it out with a knife. A set of cards tied with matching ribbon would make a good gift.

You will need:
A potato

Biscuit cutters

Knife

Paint and saucer

Sponge

Paper

1 Begin by cutting a potato in half. Take the fish-shaped biscuit cutter and press it firmly into the flesh of one half of the potato. Use the knife to cut around the shape. Lift off the cutter and remove the excess potato flesh. Put a little paint onto a saucer and use the sponge to evenly distribute the paint on the stamp. Now press the stamp gently onto blue paper. Print a few fish and leave them to dry.

2 Take a white sheet of paper and fold it in half to make the card. Now take a square of blue paper slightly smaller than the card and glue it on the front. Next glue on a small piece of gold paper. Cut out the fish print and glue it on top.

3 To finish off the picture you will need to make a simple stamp from the other half of the potato. Use the knife to cut a weed shape. Spread green paint on the stamp and print leaves of seaweed onto the card. Leave to dry.

Protect your work surface with newspaper or a plastic cloth before you begin.

It is a good idea to practise stamping your design on some scrap paper to get an idea of how much paint you need to apply to the stamp.

PAPER AND RIBBON
Gift Bags

Pack your Christmas gifts in these brightly coloured paper bags. You can make them almost any size. Use one layer of paper for smaller bags and a double layer to make larger bags. You could decorate the paper before you begin. Make a stencil to decorate the paper if you are making a lot of bags all to match for party favours. The bag handles can be made from string or pretty ribbon. Have a look around for paper decorated on both sides, or use gold or silver paper.

You will need:

A selection of paper

Glue

Hole punch

Ribbon

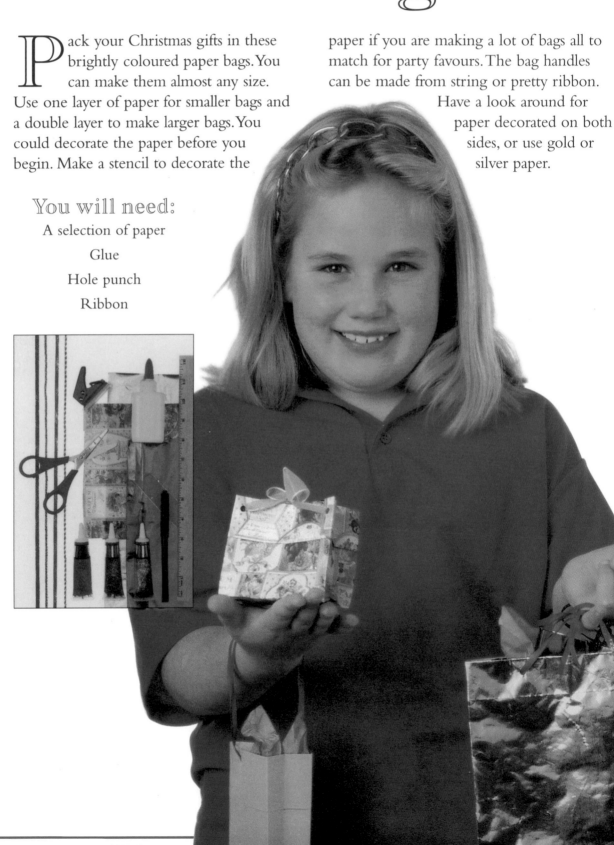

1 Begin by folding the paper in by about one quarter of its length. Run your thumbnail along the fold to mark it well.

2 Turn the folded sheet of paper over and apply glue to one end.

3 Glue the edges together to form a cylinder shape. Allow the glue to dry.

4 Flatten the cylinder shape. Run your thumbnail along the edges to make a good fold.

5 Fold about one quarter over on each side.

6 Open the two folds and press them inwards. You should now have a bag shape.

7 Make a fold upwards to form the base of the bag. Glue it down.

8 Use a hole punch to make holes to thread a ribbon through and make a handle.

Cut-out Cards

Make a row of paper flowerpots and turn them into a birthday card, or a row of blue and white teapots to send as an invitation to tea. The Christmas tree cards can be decorated as brightly as you wish and the colourful fish swimming around in their bowls will brighten up the mantlepiece. Cut-out cards are quick and easy to make and decorate. When choosing the shape remember that the card will need to be cut out so draw a compact picture. A Christmas tree cut from plain white paper and decorated using a gold pen would be very stylish.

You will need:

Paper

Felt tip pens

Crayons

Scissors

Glue

Sequins to decorate

When decorating your cards try outlining coloured-in pictures with a darker shade. This will accentuate the shapes and give the cards a professional finish.

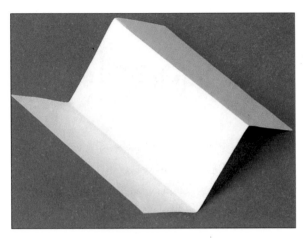

1 This card is easy to make and fun to colour, you will need a rectangle of plain white paper. Fold the sheet of paper in three to make the card shape

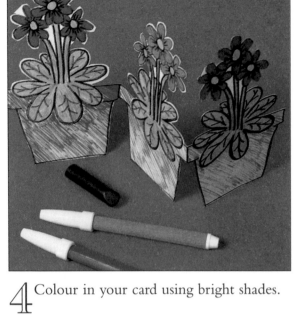

4 Colour in your card using bright shades.

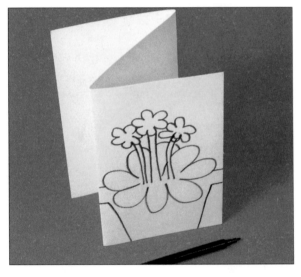

2 On the front of the card draw a pot of flowers. Make sure the flower pots are joined at the lip, or the card will fall apart when you cut it out.

5 To make this cheery Christmas card use a sheet of green paper folded in three. Draw on the Christmas tree shape and cut it out. Take care to leave the branches joined together at the base of the tree. Glue on small flowerpots cut from paper for the trees to stand in and decorate the Christmas trees with sequins and shiny stars, glued on.

3 Cut away the excess paper.

Notepaper

Fancy writing paper makes
letterwriting more fun. You can
decorate paper to suit the season:
make bright sunny pictures for summer
holiday letters and snowy scenes for winter
times. You may like to experiment with
other ideas. Maybe a seaside scene or some
rolling hills covered in tiny black sheep and
cows would suit a holiday mood. Choose
bright co-ordinated colours and matching
envelopes. Use the steely glints of shiny
gold or silver pens to create a night scene
or even to decorate a set of paper with a
firework display.

You will need:
Paper

Felt tip pens

Scissors

Glue

1 This summery style is made from green, blue and white sheets of paper. Decorate the sky-blue sheet of paper first. Cut out small fluffy white clouds and glue them onto the sky.

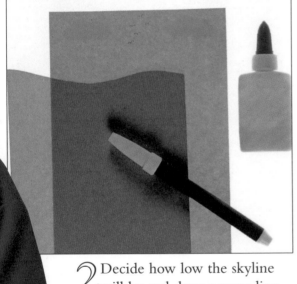

2 Decide how low the skyline will be and draw a wavy line across the green paper. Cut away the excess paper to leave grassy green hills. Lay one piece of paper on top of the other to create the scene.

3 This snowscene is decorated with a cheerful looking snowman. Draw the snowman onto a white sheet of paper. Remember to draw the horizon onto the page.

4 Use scissors to cut out the snowman and lay the sheet of white paper onto the blue sky. Decorate the snowman using a black felt tip pen, giving him a cheerful smile.

PAPER
Envelopes

You might have difficulty finding envelopes that are the correct size, especially if they are to match the paper and cards you have designed. Don't worry – there is no problem. Use these simple instructions and make envelopes to fit almost every size and shape of card. You could make the envelope from matching paper, patterned wrapping paper (you will need to attach a plain label for the address) or recycled paper. Decorate your home made envelopes using felt tip pens, stickers, paint or crayons. Remember to make the card first and use it to work around.

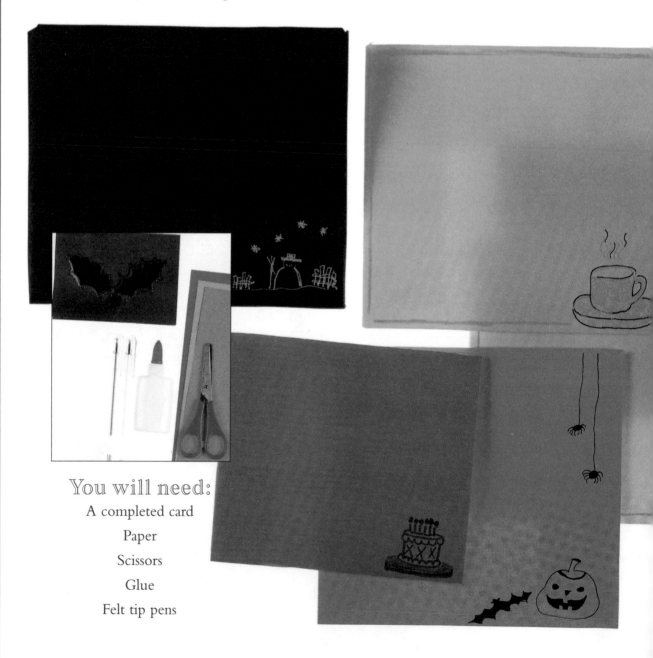

You will need:
A completed card

Paper

Scissors

Glue

Felt tip pens

1 Place the card in
the centre of the
paper. Fold the
paper up, over
the card.

2 Fold the envelope
flap down, over
the card.

3 Fold in the sides.
Make sure the card
fits the folded
shape comfortably.

4 Cut away the
excess paper from
the front of the
envelope.

5 Cut a flap shape.

6 Use glue to hold
the envelope
in shape.

Bows & Ribbons

Bows and ribbons provide the final touch to a beautifully wrapped gift. You can decorate plain ribbon with felt tip pens, creating your own designs. The ribbons shown here are decorated with tiny motor vehicles and balloons, but any design would be fun. Hallowe'en pumpkins or Christmas trees are bright and easy to draw. Bows are quick to make using the method shown. Choose thin ribbon to make small bows and wider ribbon for larger bows. Co-ordinate the patterns and colours of your home made bows with wrapping paper for a stylish look.

You will need:

Ribbon

Felt tip pens

Ruler

Scissors

Needle and thread

1 Use felt tip pens to decorate plain ribbon. Cut a little ribbon off to practise on. Press the pen down gently to prevent the colour bleeding across the weave of the ribbon.

Complete the use of one colour before moving on to the next. Remember to repeat your pattern to give the ribbon a shop bought look.

2 Spread a 60cm length of ribbon across the work surface. Use a felt tip pen and ruler to make a tiny mark every 6cm. Thread the needle with thread about 20cm longer than the ribbon and make a good knot at the end. Sew a small stitch at each mark on the ribbon. Now pull gently at the thread and the ribbon should bunch up, making a fancy bow.

Stained Glass

Create your own stained glass pictures with coloured plastic wrapping. Placed where the light shines through them these cards are most effective. Coloured wrapping film is available from craft shops, however you might want to save sweet wrappers and keep an eye out for coloured clear plastic to recycle. The holly leaves make a good Christmas card. You can have fun decorating the card with coloured glitter glue.

You will need:

Black paper

Felt tip pen

Scissors

Coloured clear wrapping

Glue and glitter glue

1 To make this clear blue fish bowl card begin by folding a sheet of white paper in half. Draw on a simple fish bowl shape and cut it out.

3 Use glitter glue to fill the bowl with fish, coloured seaweed and pebbles. Don't forget to paint on air bubbles. Decorate the edge of the bowl as well.

2 Cut a rectangle of blue coloured wrapping slightly larger than the fish bowl. Glue the rectangle onto the inside of the card, covering the fish bowl shape. Fold the card closed. You will decorate the cover of the card.

4 You will need a sheet of black paper folded in half to make the holly card. Begin by cutting out the holly leaves and berries. Cut green coloured wrapping slightly larger than the cut-out leaves and glue it to the inside of the card. Use red wrapping for the berries. Fold the card to close it and decorate the stained glass-effect card with coloured glitter glue.

If you do not have glitter glue, make your own. Use PVA glue and mix in an equal amount of fine glitter. Use a fine paint-brush to apply the glitter glue to your model or card.

CARD AND PAPER

Concertina Cards

Make one of these cards and watch the concertina movement when you open and close the card. The clown gives a good impression of playing his concertina, and the ballerina's tutu stands proudly out. The poodle's ruff looks almost real! The cards are quite simple to make, so think up some ideas of your own. You could use the concertina shape to make a bumble bee's body, or maybe a wriggly worm holding an umbrella! Use a little imagination and some brightly coloured paper to create a novel concertina card for a friend's birthday.

1 Fold a sheet of paper in half to form the card. Use the ruler to measure where to fix the concertina ends. Mark the two points, which should be evenly spaced on either side of the central fold.

2 Draw the clown with the arms ending at the dots. Make the picture quite simple.

3 Colour in your picture with bright shades, making it as attractive as possible.

4 You will need to cut a long narrow strip of yellow paper to make the concertina. Fold it to form a fan. When folding paper always use your thumbnail to press the fold firmly down.

5 Use glue to attach each end of the concertina to the end of the clown's arms.

You will need:

Paper

Ruler

Felt tip pens

Scissors

Glue

Bon Bon Plate

Make this golden plate and load it with sweeties for the party table. The plate is made using a china or metal plate with a wide edge as a mould. Use the plate to hold wrapped sweets or small cakes in paper cases. A gold plate of home made goodies would make a lovely gift.

1 The plate will be your mould for the papier mâché. Begin by covering the plate completely with clingfilm. Use white glue to stick a layer of paper squares onto the clingfilm covered plate. You will need to stick the squares completely up to the edge. Leave it to dry and then apply the next layer of newspaper squares. You will need to stick on at least 6 layers to make a plate strong enough to carry the sweets.

2 When the papier mâché is completely dry lift off the plate and peel away the clingfilm. Cut a zig zag pattern around the edge of the plate and paint the plate gold.

You will need:

A plate with a wide edge
Newspaper squares
Glue
Clingfilm
Paint-brush
Scissors
Gold paint

At the Seaside

DRIFTWOOD
Boats

When you go for a walk along the beach keep your eyes open for unusual items. This is called beachcombing. Driftwood is often washed up on the shore and collecting it is great fun, but what can you do with all those oddly shaped pieces of wood? Making small boats is one way of using them. The sails and flags can be cut from coloured tissue paper. You could make a miniature fleet of small craft and feature them on a sunny windowsill. You will need your imagination to create interesting boats, masts and sails. If you want to join pieces together, you will need to use a strong glue. Driftwood often looks good left a natural colour. However it sometimes needs decorating.

You will need:

Selection of driftwood pieces

Tissue paper

Sturdy scissors

Glue

Tissue paper

Paint

Paint-brush

Emery board

1 When making driftwood boats spend a lot of time planning the best use of particular pieces of wood you may have found. Occasionally you will find one that needs just a sail or a dot of paint to turn it into an interesting craft.

Sometimes you will need to change the shape of a piece of wood; strong scissors may do. Try using an emery board or a small piece of sandpaper to shape pieces to fit neatly together. Most of all you need to enjoy being creative with your seaside materials.

When beachcombing take care you do not injure yourself. Wear beachshoes and use rubber gloves. Check found items for nails and do not touch anything you don't recognize.

FABRIC PAINT
Beach Shoes

Beach shoes are very useful, but usually come in rather dull black or white. Use fabric paints to decorate them. The fabric paints used in this project are available from craft and fabric shops and are easy to use. It is a good idea to practise first on a piece of card. Try out a few designs. Fish or flowers make good patterns. Choose a pattern that is easy to repeat.

You will need:
Canvas shoes

Fabric paint

Be sure to clean up any spills as they occur. Don't forget to leave your work area tidy.

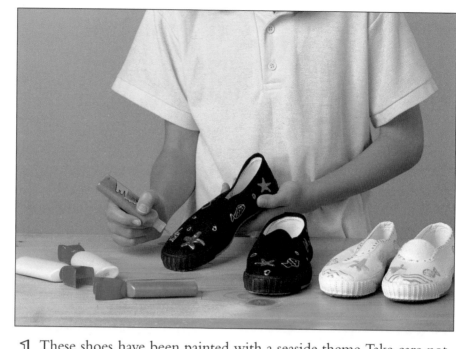

1 These shoes have been painted with a seaside theme. Take care not to smudge the decoration as you go along. When you have completed the first shoe use it as a pattern for the other one. In that way you will be able to create a matching design. Once your shoes are decorated leave them in a safe place to dry completely before you wear them on your next beachcombing expedition.

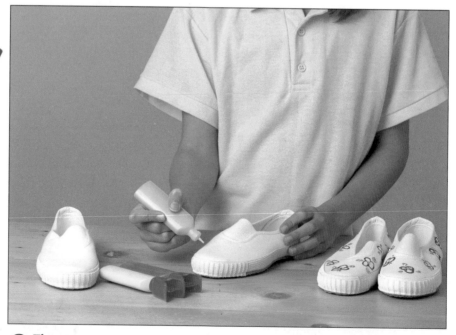

2 Flower patterns are easy to draw on and look very attractive. Decorate a pair of shoes to wear during the summer months. You could take inspiration from a special dress or T-shirt.

CARD AND PAPER
Photo Album

Seaside holidays are best remembered in photographs. Make one of these albums to keep your photographs safe. Choose bright nautical colours; blue and yellow are fun. The albums are made from card and coloured cord holds the pages together. Try making a seaside collage to decorate the cover. A beach scene or a gaily coloured yacht would look good.

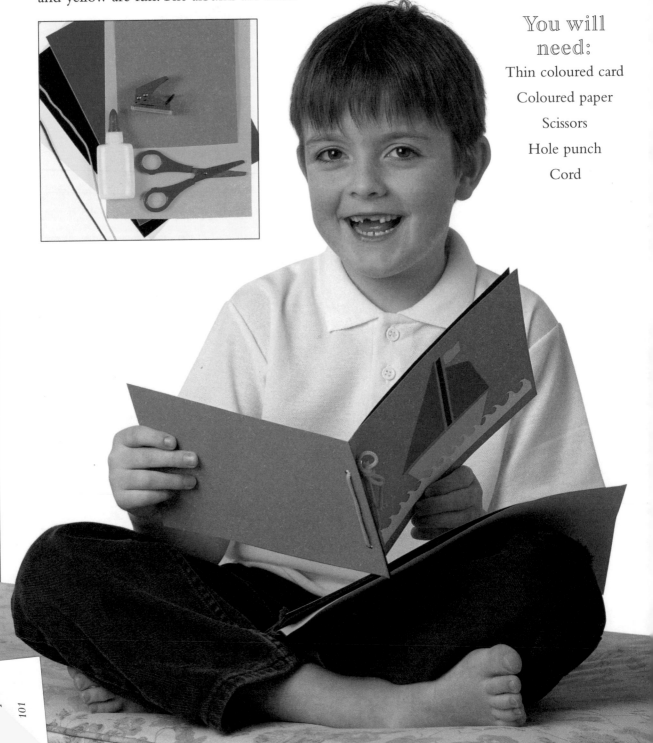

You will need:
Thin coloured card

Coloured paper

Scissors

Hole punch

Cord

1 Cut the covers and pages to size. Use the hole punch to make holes through the covers and pages. You will need to take care that they line up. Thread coloured cord through the holes to hold the album together securely and tie a bow.

2 To make the photograph holders cut a narrow strip of paper. Fold the paper inwards to create a corner sleeve. Cut away any excess paper and glue the sleeve onto the page. Do this four times, one for each corner then insert the photograph.

3 Decorate the cover of your album with an attractive seaside collage. Use coloured paper to create this yacht and cut out a row of waves to glue along the bottom of the page.

CARD, STRIP-WOOD AND OVEN BAKE CLAY
Three-in-a-row

Three-in-a-row is a good game to both make and to play. Once you have made a board you can make a selection of counters, different sets to suit different occasions. The boards are made from card and craft wood while the counters are made from oven bake clay.

Matching shells make good counters too. To play the game you need two players. Each player takes turns placing a counter on the board. You must both try to take defensive action when it's your turn, to prevent the other player from getting three-in-a-row. The first player to get a row wins.

You will need:
Thick coloured card

Craft strip-wood

Scissors

Paint-brush

Oven bake clay

Shells

Glue

1 Begin by painting the craft strip-wood in your chosen colour. Choose a colour that co-ordinates with the thick coloured card you will use for the base of the board. Leave it until it is thoroughly dry.

3 Attach the sides to the board with glue. Cut the board markings from thin strip-wood and glue these in place. Make sure you position them correctly on the board.

2 The size of your games board is decided by the piece of thick coloured card. This will need to be square. Cut the sides for your board to length from the craft strip-wood, using your board as a pattern.

4 Glue on the cross markings. Don't worry if your paintwork gets a little scratched. Once the glue is dry you can use paint to touch up any spots that might need it.

5 These noughts and crosses counters are made from oven bake clay. Use different colours and check that the counters fit the available space on the board. Try your hand at making little boats, dolphins and starfish as a variation from flat counters.

PAINTED PEBBLES
Paperweights

Pebble painting is fun and a good rainy day activity. Collect pebbles along the beach and save them. When you want to enjoy a quiet time get out the paints and your imagination, and make these attractive paperweights. You could paint a tiny row of pebble cottages (use a fine paint-brush to paint on tiny windows and doors) and little rose bushes along the cottage front. Or try your hand at painting a tiny kitten on a pebble or a fish or even a skeleton.

1 These interesting decorations need a little time and practice. Wash and dry the pebbles before you begin. Use a fine paint-brush to paint in the detail. Once you are happy with your chosen decoration and the paint has dried, add a layer of varnish.

2 A row of painted pebble cottages makes a good ornamental display. Choose pebbles which have suitable shapes and which can stand up. You may need to apply two coats of paint to the house and roof to give a good surface for decorating. When you have painted the cottages give them a coat of varnish to protect them and to give them a glossy finish.

You will need:
Pebbles

Paint, varnish and paint-brushes

Flowerpots

Flowerpots look good sitting along a sunny windowsill. Fill them with brightly coloured flowers to bring a little of the garden indoors. These pots are decorated with shells bought from a specialist craft shop. The shells are all recycled. The creatures that used to live in them are used as food in some countries and the shells simply thrown away. Ask at your local craft shops for them. If you gather them yourself, always check that you are allowed to on that particular beach.

You will need:

Shells

Terracotta pot or container to recycle

Grout

Spatula

Paint

Paint-brush

Glue

Varnish

1 Choose your plant pot and shells. Use a
spatula to apply a layer of grout along the
rim of the pot. Press the shells firmly into
the grout. Leave the grout to dry. When it is
dry you may want to apply a little varnish to
bring out the colours of the shells.

2 These pretty pink pots have been
decorated with tiny shells. Begin by
painting the pot pink. You may need
two coats of paint. After the paint is dry use
strong glue to attach the shells. When the glue
has set apply a layer of varnish to the shells.

CARD AND GLITTER
Aquarium

The fish floating in this model aquarium are made from thin card and decorated with paint and glitter. They shimmer through the weed and clear blue sea very realistically when you gently shake the box. Use a large shoe box to make the aquarium. You could make a shoal of tiny fish to weave their way through the weed. The fish are suspended from the ceiling of the box with thin gold thread which is almost invisible. Place a few rocks and shells in the bottom of the box. If you have one, a model shipwreck would make an attractive feature.

You will need:
Large shoebox

Scissors

Paint & paint-brush

Blue plastic film

Tissue paper

Thin card and paper

Felt tip pens

Glue

Glitter

Gold thread

Pebbles

1 Cut a rectangle from the box lid.

2 Cut a rectangle from the base of the box.

3 Paint the box and lid blue, inside and out.

4 Glue blue film over the cut-out spaces.

5 Cut strips of tissue paper for weeds. Glue them in place suspended from the roof of the aquarium. Use two colours of green.

6 Draw fish on the thin card and decorate them with paint and glitter. Attach them to the lid of the box with gold thread.

Fishing Game

Fishing games always go down well at parties and games evenings. This fishing game is quite easy to make. The fish hooks and the fish mouths are made from paper clips. You could also make fish in two colours or make several different sea creatures, such as fish and starfish. Then players can see how many of each they can 'catch' in a given time. Another game might be to give each fish a value, adding the values at the end of the game to see which 'catch' is worth the most. This would introduce gamesmanship as each player goes for the highest value catch.

You will need:

Plate

Thick card

Thin card

Scissors

Glue

Sticky tape

Ruler

Felt tips

Sticks

String

Paper clips

1 Use a plate as an outline for a circular shape on a piece of thick card. Cut out the circle. This will be the base of the pond. Measure out a long strip of thin card for the sides. Tape it to the base.

2 The sides of the pond will prevent the fish from jumping out! Use coloured tape or felt tip pens to decorate the sides.

3 Draw the fish and starfish on a piece of thick card and decorate them using felt tip pens. Cut them out. You will need to make quite a few fish and starfish.

4 Now make the loops on the decorated stars and fish from paper clips. You will need to fold up a section of the paper clip and attach it with sticky tape to the fish and starfish.

5 The fishing rods are made from garden sticks. Tie a piece of string to one end of each stick and a paper clip to the end of each piece of string. Shape the paper clip into a hook.

SEASHELL
Treasure Boxes

Shells can be used decoratively in so many ways. In this project they are used to decorate a small storage box and to make a pretty circular picture frame. You will need an empty cheese box and some shells to make the storage box plus some grout or strong glue to attach the shells. You can arrange them in a regular pattern or randomly over the lid. The picture frame is made from thin card.

You will need:

Empty cheese box

Selection of shells

Grout

Spatula

Thin card

Scissors

Varnish

Paint-brush

If you do not have any grout you could use some strong glue.

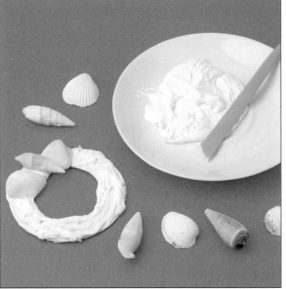

1 First check that the box is clean. Before you begin, experiment with the design. Lay the shells on the lid without any grout. When you are happy with the design spread a layer of grout across the box lid using the spatula and gently press the shells in place.

3 To make this pretty shell encrusted picture frame you will need a circle of thin card with a hole cut out of the centre. This will make the frame shape. Apply a layer of grout using the spatula and gently press the shells into an attractive pattern around the edge.

2 Leave the box in a warm airy spot to dry. You will need to give the shell covered box plenty of time to dry off. When it is dry paint on a layer of varnish to give the shells an attractive finish.

4 When the grout has dried the frame is ready for a layer of varnish. This will protect it and bring out the colours. Now you can insert a photograph and hang up the frame or use it as a small paperweight.

Tablemats

Mosaics are usually created using small square tiles. To make these tablemats we have cut lots of small squares from paper and used them glued onto sugar paper to create a fishy picture. Choose bright colours to create your pictures. Squares cut from magazine pictures can also be used to make mosaics. The important thing to remember, when making a mosaic, is to keep the lines straight. This gives the impression of tiles all lined up. Use a ruler and pencil to make markings on your paper so that you can keep the squares neat and in order.

You will need:
Paper
Ruler
Pencil
Scissors
Glue

1 Begin by drawing a simple outline of a fish on your paper. Make sure that the picture is centrally placed.

2 Use the ruler and pencil to measure out squares and cut them out in your chosen colours. You will need a lot of squares.

3 Glue on the squares. Begin in a corner of the picture and try to work from one side of the picture to the other.

4 Your finished fish mosaic should look something like this. You could make a set of table mats for the family.

5 For a special event you might want to decorate some table napkins to match your table mats. Use paper and create pretty collage pictures.

Pencil Wallet

Clear plastic wallets can be decorated with glass paints to create your own personal style. This wallet has been designed to give the impression of a fish bowl, with two brightly coloured fish. File wallets can be personalised with glass paint. Black outliner is great for a labelling design. Different subject folders would look good with a decorated title. Enjoy practising your creative skills on different plastic containers.

1 Before you start on a design make sure the plastic wallet or folder is completely clean. Try out a few design ideas on paper first, practising the shapes. Use the outliner to mark out your design on the wallet or folder. The outliner will take an hour or so to dry. When it is dry paint on the colour with a clean dry brush. Do one colour at a time and clean the brush carefully between colours.

You will need:
A clear plastic wallet
Glass paints
Black outliner
Kitchen paper to mop up any spills

Toys and Games

Snake

This beautiful sinuous snake can be made from bottle tops. You will need to collect a lot of bottle tops, so it may be worth asking friends to save them for you. By combining different coloured tops you could create a multi-coloured snake and if you saved only one colour of bottle tops your snake would still be dramatic. The silver shimmers and the closely fitted bottle tops give the appearance of scales when wriggled along the floor. The snake's head is made from a cork and his bright red tongue is a piece of felt, cut to shape and pushed into the cork.

You will need:

Hammer

Large nail

Piece of wood

Bottle tops

Strong string

Scissors

Cork

Glue

Paint & paint-brushes

Small piece of felt

1 Hammer a nail through a piece of wood near its end. You can then hold the wood and position the nail to make the hole in the centre of the bottle top.

When all the bottle tops have holes in them thread them onto the string. Think about your colour co-ordination. A snake like this one will need approximately 70 bottle tops.

2 Attach a piece of cork to each end of the string of bottle tops. One end will be the tail – paint it green. The other end will be the head – paint this green as well and add two spots for the eyes. Cut a small piece of felt into the shape of a snake's tongue and press it into the cork with the point of the nail.

PLASTIC CONTAINERS AND OVEN BAKE CLAY
Skittles

Enjoy a game of skittles whenever you like with these brightly decorated recycled drink containers. You will need six containers to make a set. Paint them in bright colours and decorate them with coloured stars. If they get knocked over too easily, pour some sand into each one to make them heavier. Mini- or table-skittles can also be fun. You could make a set to take away on holiday. They are made from oven bake clay. Take turns with a friend to see how many skittles you can knock down with each shot.

You will need:
Empty drink containers

Paint

Paint-brushes

Sand, for weight

To make mini-skittles you will need:

Oven bake clay

1 Wash out the drink containers well. Leave upside down to drain. Screw the lids on tightly and your skittles are ready for painting. Begin by painting a base coat.

You may need two layers of paint. When the base coat is dry, paint on the decoration. When all your skittles are painted and decorated they are ready for use.

2 To make these mini-skittles you will need oven bake clay in three colours. Divide the clay into equal pieces and shape the skittles. Use oven bake clay of a different colour to make flattened ball shapes and press them onto the skittles. Shape a ball and when your ball and skittles are ready, bake in the oven according to the manufacturer's directions. You might want to decorate a small box in which to store your mini-skittles.

A set of mini-skittles would make a good Christmas cracker gift or party favour.

A full size set of skittles could be used at a school games day or fund raising event.

Magic Pictures

This fishy picture changes from black and white to colour quite magically. Make one to delight a younger brother or sister. Choose your picture carefully: an empty black and white hillside could turn into a green pasture covered with sheep, or a bare table top could have a birthday cake appear on it.

Use brightly coloured felt tip pens to colour your picture. It is a good idea to keep the shapes simple. If you don't have a plastic folder you might be able to recycle a piece of clear plastic from a carton.

You will need:

Thin card or paper

Scissors

Marker and felt tip pens

Plastic folder

Sticky tape

1 Take a sheet of thin card or paper and fold it carefully into three equal sections as shown in the picture.

2 On the front flap mark out a rectangle and the finger grip space. Cut away the finger grip space.

3 Open out the card and cut out the rectangle. This is the front of the card.

4 Draw a decorative border on this front frame. Cut a separate piece of paper the same size as one section of the card and draw on your design, using felt tip pens.

5 Slip your picture into the plastic folder with the top against a fold. Trim the plastic to the picture. Stick the back to the plastic.

6 Use a marker pen to draw an outline of the picture on the plastic. Now take your card and open it out flat.

7 Fold the bottom flap into the middle. Slip the plastic-covered picture over the bottom flap. The bottom flap is now between the coloured picture and the outlined picture on the plastic flap. Fold the top flap down over the plastic. Grip the plastic and paper and pull; the picture will appear in colour as you pull it out.

CARD AND OVEN BAKE CLAY
Games Board

This neat little games board is made from thick card and a piece of narrow craft wood. You will need a little time and patience to paint the squares neatly but it is worthwhile when you consider the entertainment you will get from a home made games board. Here we show how you can make home made draughts from oven bake clay. You could use two colours of buttons or pebbles instead. Maybe you have a small set of chess pieces at home that could be used. A personalized board would make a lovely present.

You will need:

A small board-shaped piece of thick card

Paint & paint-brushes

Pencil

Ruler

Scissors

Thin piece of strip wood from a craft shop

Glue

Oven bake clay

Match box

1 Paint the card in a light colour. Paint the strip wood in a darker colour. Leave to dry in a safe spot. When the paint is dry, carefully mark out the games board with eight rows of eight squares. Use the ruler to measure the squares. Leave space at each end of the board to keep pieces not in use during the game.

2 When you are satisfied with the marked areas, paint in the darker colour. When the paint is dry, use the scissors to cut the strip wood and glue into shape to form an edge around the board. Decorate the board with an attractive pattern at each end and touch up any parts of the edging that need painting.

3 Shape the draughts from oven bake clay. You will need eight counters in each colour. It is best to roll out a sausage shape of clay and cut slices to size. Bake them in the oven following the manufacturer's directions. Paint a small matchbox in the darker colour and decorate it to match your games board. Use the box to store your draughts.

If you had an old tea tray you might want to recycle it into a games board. Ask an adult for help; you may need to sand the tray down with sandpaper first as well as decorate it using several coats of paint!

Doll's House

Make a cute little doll's house for a miniature doll or bear to live in. This house is made from two boxes. Use any card you may have over to make miniature furniture. You may want to have a look round for some small matchboxes or other containers to recycle as furniture. Coloured paper makes good wallpaper, as does wrapping paper. Use a piece of fabric to make carpets and rugs, and don't forget some pictures to go on the walls. Decorate the outside of your house with paint, creating a cheerful summery scene for your doll to live in.

You will need:

Two shoeboxes

Scissors

Tape & glue

Large paper clips

Paint & paint-brushes

Paper & card

Small boxes

Felt tip pens

1 Use one of the boxes to make the house. Cut a corner off the other box to make the roof and cut the lid so that it fits inside the house as the upstairs floor.

2 Place the shoe box that will be the house up on one end. Use tape to attach the roof piece you have prepared at an angle to the top of the house. Use glue and tape to stick the floor section into place. Hold the floor in position with the large paperclips while the glue is setting.

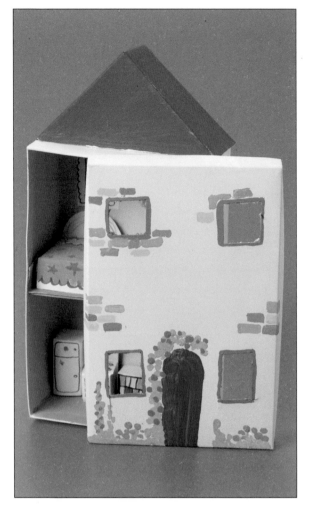

3 When the glue is set your house is ready to decorate. Paint the roof a rich reddy brown and the walls pale pink. Make a front for the house from the other shoe-box lid and cut out windows. Paint a bright front door and flowers and make your house summery and cheerful.

4 Miniature furniture is easy to make from scraps of paper and small boxes. Cover boxes with white paper to make kitchen equipment and coloured paper for furniture in other rooms. Use felt tip pens to outline shapes and decorate the pieces. Don't forget wallpaper and rugs and maybe some pictures on the walls.

Blow Football

Football is a very popular sport. Enjoy a game of blow football on a rainy day by making your own table sized football pitch. This pitch has been made with a piece of sponge board. If you wanted to make a more long lasting pitch, you could get an adult to help prepare a piece of chipboard or plywood. You will also need green felt to cover the board although paint would give a reasonable surface. The game is played using drinking straws and table tennis balls. Each player begins with an equal number of balls and sees how many he or she can blow into the opposite goal. Once you become more professional, you might want to play a more traditional football game with one ball decorated using a marker pen to look like a real football.

You will need:

Sponge board

Green felt

Scissors

Glue

Shaped craft strip wood

Paint

Paint-brushes

Cocktail sticks

Coloured paper

A shoebox

Drinking straws

Table tennis balls

1 Cut out the felt slightly larger than the board. Spread the board with glue and press the felt onto the board.

3 Glue the edging in place and use the white paint to mark out the goal mouths and centre line.

2 Cut the edging to size and paint it yellow. As well as both sides and ends of the pitch, you will need four small pieces to make the corners.

4 Press a cocktail stick into each corner of your pitch. Fold the coloured paper in half and cut out four flag shapes. Glue the flags onto the cocktail sticks.

5 Cut the shoebox in half. Paint the halves white and when they are dry place them on the pitch at opposite goal mouths. Put the table tennis balls in position and it's time to challenge someone to a game!

CARDBOARD
Toy Cars

These cute little cars are great fun to make and given a push will whizz along a smooth surface. The wheels are made from milk or juice container lids, cocktail sticks and straws. The car chassis is cut from either coloured card or the sides of a recycled grocery box.

You will need:

Thick card

Scissors

Masking tape

Paint

Paint-brushes

Four juice or milk carton lids

Straws

Cocktail sticks

1 Begin by drawing two side views of a car. Cut them out. Next cut out a long rectangular shape. The width of the rectangle decides how wide the car is.

2 Use the scissors to cut out two small v-shapes to form the wheel arches. The wheel axles will run through these v-shapes. The wheel axles will be held in place by the base of the car.

3 Now you are ready to assemble your car. Use masking tape to attach the long rectangular shape to the car sides. Do this and you will see the car take shape.

4 Cut a piece of card to fit in the base of the car. Tape it in place. Your car is now ready to paint and decorate. You could paint on a family sitting in the car.

5 To make the wheels each lid will need a hole made through its centre. Push the end of a straw through the hole. Now use a cocktail stick to hold it in place. Break the ends off so that the wheel turns.

6 Push the wheel axle all the way through and attach the second wheel. Cut off any long pieces of straw to fit the car. Now make and fit the second axle.

Party Hats

Making party hats is a great way of getting the party spirit going. These hats are quite easy to make from card and crêpe paper, and can be decorated with glitter and junk jewelry.

Try your hand at making a complete set of party hats for a special family meal or celebration. Make Queen and King crowns for the grown-ups and fancy coronets or colourful jester's hats for all the children.

You will need:

Thin card

Scissors

Needle and thread

Crêpe paper

Glue

Glitter

Hair band for the tiara

1 Cut a length of card that will go around your head with a small overlap.

2 Next cut a wide piece of crêpe paper the length of the card. This will need to be quite wide; have a look at the illustration to get an idea of the size. Sew a line of running stitch along one of the long sides of the crêpe paper.

3 Glue the crêpe paper onto the card.

Paint pasta shapes gold or silver and decorate with glitter and use to decorate your crown.

4 Next, glue the paper-covered card into a hat shape. Pull the ends of the thread to gather the crêpe paper and tie a knot. Use crêpe paper to cover a small disc shape of card and glue that over the centre of the hat. Decorate the hat with coloured paper or card and glitter.

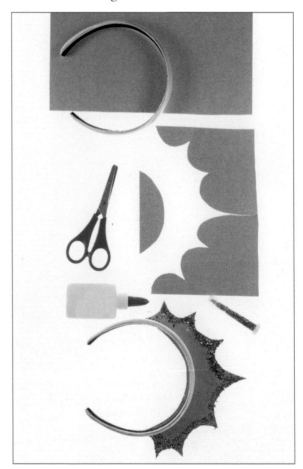

5 This sparkling tiara is made with a hair band and gold card. Lay the hair band onto the card and draw out the shape. Cut out the tiara shape and decorate it with glitter. Attach the tiara to the hair band and leave to dry.

SHOEBOX
Model Theatre

Make a model theatre and stage your own pantomime this Christmas. You will need a shoebox and coloured paper to make the theatre. Once you have decided on a storyline you can get a script together and decorate sheets of paper to use as scenery.

Make small model trees and furnishings from card and paper. Cut out actors from thin card and use sticky tape to attach them to sticks. You can have as many actors on the stage as you can handle. So you may need a friend or two to help when staging your big production.

1 You will need a shoebox to make your theatre. Stand it on its side and cut out an opening on each end. Your actors will enter the stage from these openings.

2 Use coloured paper to decorate the front of the theatre. Make curtains and frills. Use a black felt tip pen to mark out the gathers. Accentuate the edges with glitter.

3 Glue the curtains into place using sticky tape for difficult corners.

4 Cut a piece of paper to size and decorate it with crayons to make a scene that suits your play. Attach it to the back of the box; this will be your scenery backdrop.

5 Cut out coloured paper shapes that match your scenery. Use sticky tape to attach them to the inside edges of the curtains; these are called the wing flats.

6 Draw your actors onto thin card cut out from the lid of the shoebox. Colour them in using felt tip pens and cut them out. Use sticky tape to attach them to the sticks. Remember they will have to enter the stage through the side entrances, so check for height.

Cloth Doll

A soft cloth doll is nice to cuddle up to and looks pretty lying on a pillow as decoration. These dolls are made from cotton fabric and are cut out in a 'gingerbread man' shape. Their hair is made from wool and they are dressed in simply shaped clothes tied with ribbon. A cloth doll can be made large, as a bed decoration or tiny, to live in a doll's house or be a 'pocket' doll. Practise painting faces on a piece of paper to get the shapes right before you paint your doll's face on.

You will need:

Fabric in a flesh colour for the doll

Felt tip pen

Scissors

Needle and thread

Polyester stuffing

Paint

Paint-brush

Wool

Ribbon

Patterned fabric for the doll's dress

1 Draw a doll shape onto a double layer of fabric. Remember you will need a neck shape that you can sew around and cut out. Look carefully at the picture to get an idea of the shape you need to draw.

2 Sew around the drawn line, remembering to leave a gap to turn the fabric out. Fill it with stuffing, then cut the doll shape out.

3 Use the cut-out doll as a pattern to cut a simple dress shape and sew the edges.

4 Turn the dress the right way out and sew a hem along the bottom of the fabric.

5 Dress your doll and paint on a face. Make hair by winding the wool around a piece of card then sewing a 'parting' across the middle. Attach the hair with glue.

6 Tie a ribbon belt in a bow around the waist. Now your doll is ready to enjoy.

Juggling Balls

Juggling is a great skill to develop. It takes time and patience but can be most fulfilling. Make yourself some juggling balls and a set for a friend and practise together. These juggling balls are made from printed cotton fabric and filled with uncooked green lentils. Lentils are a perfect filling as they will give the juggling balls some weight and be easy to grip. They are also quite economically priced – and – if you stop juggling you can cook the lentils for supper!

1 Cut a rectangle of fabric and fold it in half. Sew seams along the side edges. Sew strong stitches close together or ask an adult for help and use a sewing machine.

4 Close the bag making a triangular shape by bringing the two side seam ends together and neatly fold the edges inside to allow for the final seam.

2 Turn the bag shape right side out.

5 Sew the edge together firmly.

You will need:
Fabric

Scissors

Green lentils

Needle and thread

3 Half fill the bags with green lentils.

Juggling balls would make a great birthday gift for a friend.

FABRIC AND CARD
Doll's Bed

Y ou will need a shoebox to make this comfy bed for a doll or teddy bear. The bed is made from the box and the bedhead is made from the lid. The bed will look stylish covered with brightly coloured gingham fabric or you could decorate some plain fabric using fabric felt tip pens. Cover the fabric with small flowers or draw out a patchwork spread pattern.

You will need:

A shoebox

Fabric

Scissors

Glue

Lace

Fabric painting pens

Polyester wadding

Needle and thread

1 Turn the box upside down and cover it neatly with fabric. When attaching fabric it is a good idea to put the glue on the box rather than the fabric. Use a length of gathered lace to create a frill.

4 Gather the fabric into a frill and glue it onto the bed. Make a mattress from polyester wadding and sew on a fabric cover. Decorate the inside of the box lid to make a matching bedhead.

2 Stick a piece of matching fabric onto the inside of the lid of the shoebox to make the bedhead and glue the bedhead onto the base. Cut pieces of polyester wadding to size and sew on fabric covers to make the mattress, pillow and duvet.

5 To make the pillow cut a piece of polyester wadding to a suitable size, fold a piece of fabric over the pillow shape and cut out the cover. Decorate the pillow cover using fabric pens. Use your needle and thread to sew the pillow up.

3 The fabric to make this bed is decorated with fabric painting pens. Measure how much fabric you will need to make the frill around the bed. Decorate the frill with a scalloped pattern.

6 Make a duvet from a piece of polyester wadding and fabric. Use fabric pens to decorate the duvet cover so it looks like a patchwork quilt. Copy your scalloped design for the border.

SHOEBOX
Guessing Box

Guessing boxes, filled with interestingly shaped items such as damp squidgy sponges, fir cones or plastic spiders, can be great fun at parties. When players put their hands through the hole their imaginations will turn a damp sponge into something very strange, not the kind of thing one would normally want to touch without looking at it first! Another game to play with a guessing box is to put in a variety of similar things, such as vegetables. Then the players have to guess what they are, by touch.

1 Use the circular object to draw a hand-hole on one side of the box.

3 Paint the outside of the box and lid black. If necessary, apply two coats.

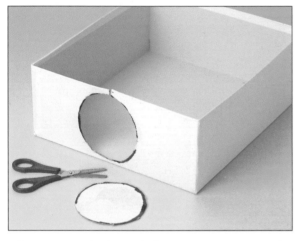

2 Cut out the hand-hole. It is easier to start the hole by cutting down from the top. This cut will be hidden by the lid.

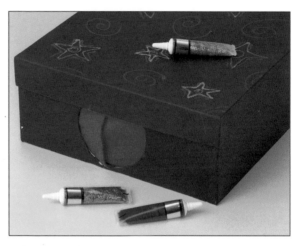

4 Use sticky tape to attach a fabric curtain in the box over the hole and decorate the box with glitter or coloured paint.

You will need:

Large shoebox

Circular object to draw around

Pen

Scissors

Paint

Paint-brush

Sticky tape

Piece of fabric

Glitter

Pick-up-Sticks

Pick-up-Sticks is a very old game. Children have played it for generations. To play you need a bundle of similar sized sticks and one pick-up-stick. The player throws the sticks onto the play area and uses the pick-up-stick to help pick up each stick individually without moving any of the others. If the player does nudge another stick her turn is over and the next player gets the sticks to start the process over again. The player who picks up the most sticks is the winner. You can play against yourself by attempting to beat your record each time you play.

1 Divide the skewers into four groups of six with one left over. You will need the felt tip pens to colour the skewers. One skewer will need to be one all over colour. This is the stick you will use to help you pick up the others in the game. Choose a different colour for each of the four groups of sticks. Colour the ends of the sticks with the felt tip pens.

2 You could make a mini pick-up-sticks set with cocktail sticks!

You will need:
25 wooden skewers
Felt tip pens

Models and Boxes

AIR HARDENING CLAY
Creepy Crawly Pots

Caterpillars, ladybirds, butterflies and flowers make brilliant decorations on small clay pots. These pots are made from air hardening clay in the shape of insects and flowers and painted in summer colours. They are great fun to make. Have a look around the garden for creatures to inspire you before you begin.

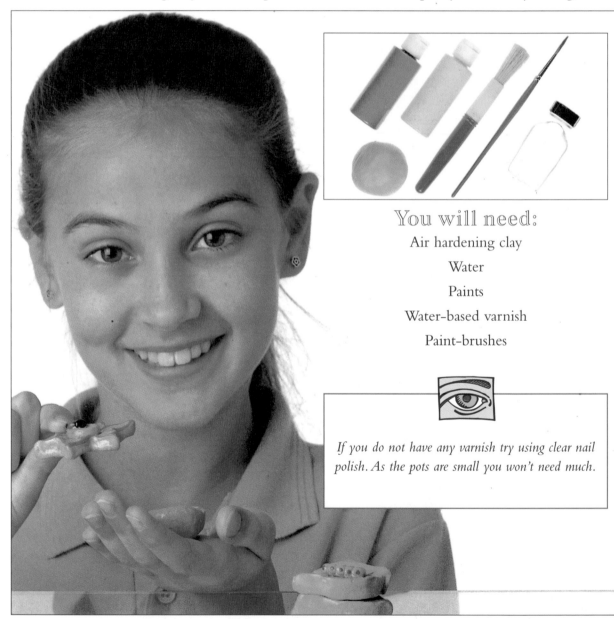

You will need:

Air hardening clay

Water

Paints

Water-based varnish

Paint-brushes

If you do not have any varnish try using clear nail polish. As the pots are small you won't need much.

1 First make the bowl of the pot, using your thumbs to shape it. Smooth the clay with your finger tips. When you are happy with the shape, make a lid to fit the bowl. Gently stretch the lid into petal shapes and make a little ladybird from two small clay balls. Use a little water to moisten the base of the ladybird before you attach it to the lid. Leave the pot in a warm airy spot to dry. When it is completely dry, paint it, allowing the paint to dry between colours. When the paint is dry, varnish your pot to give it a professional finish.

3 The caterpillar on this pot is made from small balls of clay, all joined up with water. When it is dry, decorate the caterpillar in bright colours.

2 This ladybird pot is very easy to make. Make the base first, using your thumbs to shape it and smooth the clay with your fingertips. Make a lid to fit the base and leave the pot in a warm airy spot to dry. When it is completely dry, paint the inside and outside black. When the black is dry, paint the ladybird red, then paint on the black dots. You may need to touch up the black when it is dry.

Découpage Boxes

Découpage is the art of decorating boxes with paper cut-outs. These boxes have been decorated with pictures cut from wrapping paper. Old magazines are a good source for pictures.

Use a box with a tight lid to decorate for a gardening friend to store seeds in, or decorate to hold special handmade decorations for the Christmas tree.

You will need:

Boxes to decorate

Glue

Newspaper

Paint

Paint-brushes

Scissors

Pictures cut from wrapping paper

Water-based varnish

1 Make sure your chosen box is clean inside. Glue on a layer of newspaper squares to cover the box. Leave it in a warm airy spot to dry.

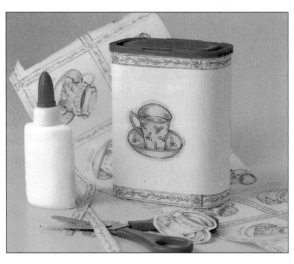

3 When the paint is completely dry, the box is ready to decorate. Cut carefully around the pictures, glue on the border and then the feature picture.

2 When the papier mâché layer is dry, paint on a base coat of colour. You may need two coats to make a good surface to decorate.

4 When the glue is set, the box is ready to varnish. It will need two coats to give it a professional finish.

Decorate small wooden boxes to use for jewelry. Clean up the wood with sandpaper first, then glue on your pictures. Apply two coats of varnish when the glue is dry.

Jewellery Box

Keep your jewellery safe in one of these sparkling treasure troves. The boxes are made from thick card and decorated with gold and silver paint, glitter, glass beads and recycled junk jewellery. If you don't have any suitable old jewels, use brightly decorated gold or silver buttons or sequins.

You will need:

Thick card

Scissors

Sticky tape and glue

Newspaper

Gold paint and glitter

Shiny buttons or jewellery to recycle

1 Cut a base and lid from thick card. Use the base to measure the size of the walls of the box.

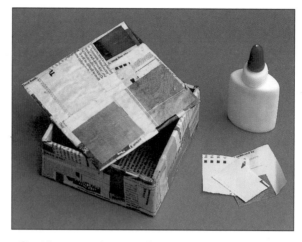

3 Glue two layers of squares cut from the newspaper onto the box and lid. Leave in a warm airy spot to dry.

2 Stick the shapes together to form the box. Use glue or sticky tape.

4 When the papier mâché layer is dry, it is ready to decorate. Paint the box inside and out with gold paint. It may need two coats. When the paint is dry, decorate the lid with glitter, paint and jewels.

Remember to protect the work surface with newspaper before you begin.

MATCHBOX
Chest of Drawers

The decorations on these tiny chests of drawers give you a good idea of the contents. The chests of drawers are useful for storing stamps or buttons and are made from empty matchboxes, covered with sticky-backed paper. You may want to make a set of drawers for the toolbox to store small nails and screws. The button drawers would be good for saving odd buttons from the sewing box and stamp collectors would find the stamp drawers very useful. You could even make a tiny chest of drawers and decorate it to put in the doll's house bedroom.

You will need:

Empty matchboxes

Glue

Scissors

Sticky-backed paper

Felt

Selection of buttons and stamps

Thin wire (fuse wire would do well)

Saucer of water

Paper fasteners

1 To make the button storage drawers, begin by gluing the three matchboxes, one on top of another. When the glue has dried, cover the set of drawers with sticky-backed paper. Spread the box with glue, then stick on the felt covering. Dab on a little glue and stick on the buttons, one at a time. To make handles for the drawers, attach buttons with a little wire.

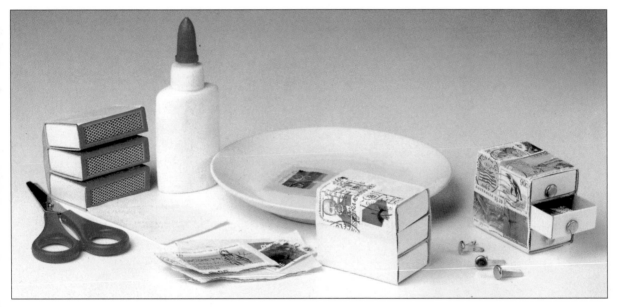

2 To make the stamp drawer you will need a selection of brightly decorated stamps. Place the stamps in a saucer of water for a few minutes to loosen the glue and remove them from the envelope paper. Glue three matchboxes one on top of another then cover the box with sticky-backed paper. Glue on the stamps, taking care to arrange them so you can see the interesting pictures on them. Make drawer handles from paper fasteners.

You could use stickers to decorate a chest of drawers or decorate the sticky-backed paper with felt tip pens.

Money Boxes

These stylishly decorated money boxes would look good in the living room. They are made from recycled containers which have good, well-fitting lids. Encourage the whole family to make savings by decorating money boxes for them all. Flowers painted pink, bright orange and yellow, or a money box that suits a particular hobby or style – you can create them easily from old boxes.

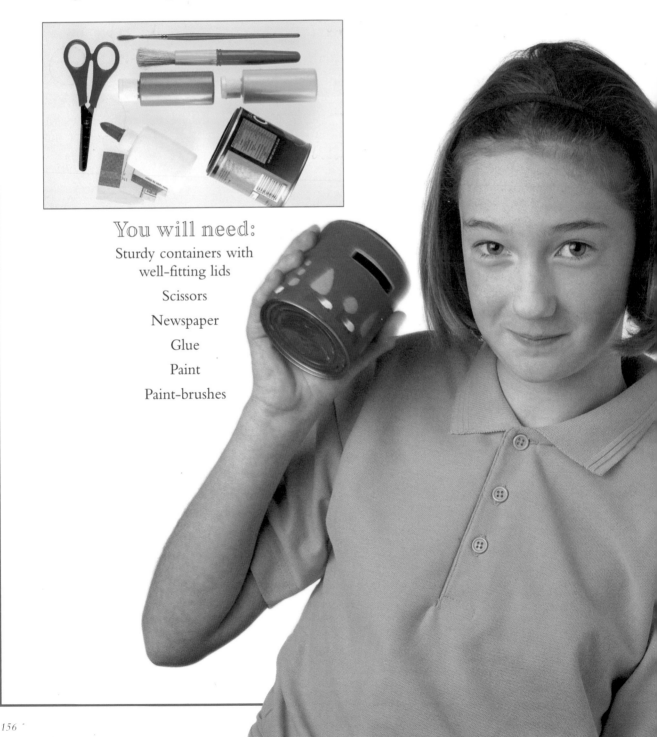

You will need:

Sturdy containers with
well-fitting lids

Scissors

Newspaper

Glue

Paint

Paint-brushes

1 You will need an adult to help you cut out the money slit. Use a large coin to help measure the space.

3 When the papier mâché is dry, paint on the base colour, then paint on tiny trees and shrubs.

2 Glue squares of newspaper onto the box to make a good painting surface.

4 These money boxes are made from cardboard boxes. Cut out a slit before covering completely with papier mâché. Once full they will need to be cut open to get at the money!

Pencil Tubs

Use paint and glitter to decorate a useful storage tub for pens and pencils. Choose a cylinder-shaped container to recycle into a pencil tub and cover it with a layer of papier mâché to make it stronger and provide a good surface to decorate.

You will need:

Cardboard containers

Newspaper

Glue

Paint

Glitter

Paint-brushes

Scissors

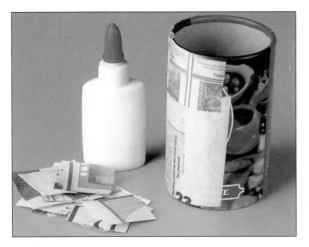

1 Start by covering the container with a layer of newspaper squares, glued on. Cover the container and leave it in a warm, airy place to dry.

2 When the papier mâché is completely dry, paint on a base coat and allow it to dry. You may need two coats of paint.

3 Paint on the fish and seaweed, using one colour at a time. Don't forget to paint on some air bubbles above the fish.

4 When the paint is dry, spread glue on areas you want to glitter and sprinkle on the glitter. Do this one colour at a time and leave it to dry between colours.

Before you begin, give the cardboard container a quick wash. Stand it upside down to drain and then dry it with a clean tea towel.

Sewing Box

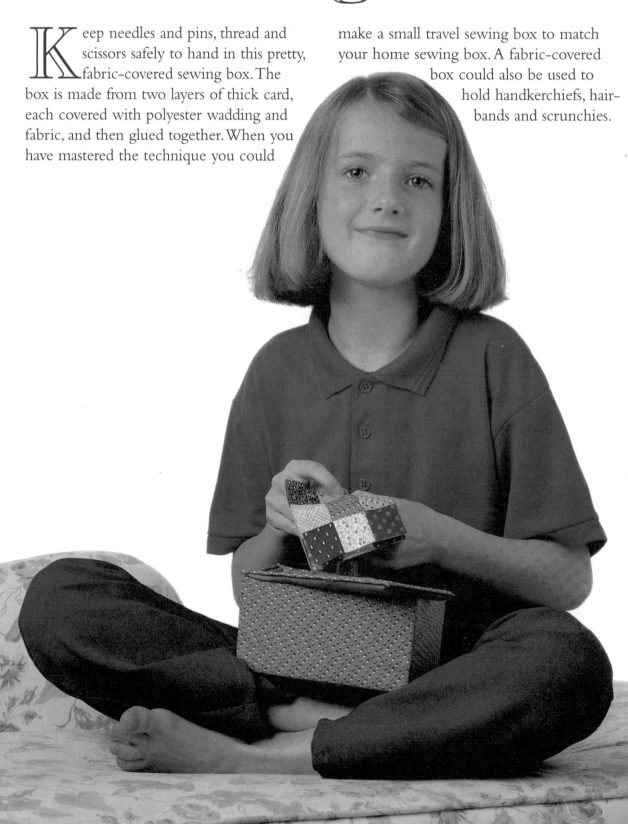

Keep needles and pins, thread and scissors safely to hand in this pretty, fabric-covered sewing box. The box is made from two layers of thick card, each covered with polyester wadding and fabric, and then glued together. When you have mastered the technique you could make a small travel sewing box to match your home sewing box. A fabric-covered box could also be used to hold handkerchiefs, hair-bands and scrunchies.

1 Decide on the size of your box. Cut the base from thick card. Use the base to measure out the sides of the box and cut the lid the same size as the base. This will be the outer box. Cut out two complete sets of card. Now cut half a centimetre off around the edge of one set of card pieces. This will be the inner box.

2 Glue a piece of wadding to the four sides of the outer box and cover each one with patterned fabric. Cover the outer lid and base pieces with patterned fabric. Glue a piece of wadding to each piece of the inner box, including the lid and base, then cover these with plain fabric. (Choose co-ordinating fabrics for a stylish effect.)

3 Glue the matching outer and inner pieces together. Glue the whole box together and hold it in place with the elastic band.

4 To decorate the lid, cover a small square piece of card with plain fabric. Glue this on to the lid. Now cut a strip of fabric, cover it with glue and fold it in half lengthways, roll it up to form a grip, and glue it on to the lid.

You will need:
Thick card

Scissors

Wadding

Half a metre of patterned fabric

Fabric glue

Half a metre of plain fabric

Elastic band

FOLDED PAPER
Origami

Paper folding is a useful skill to learn. Follow the instructions and once you have mastered them, if you have a sheet of paper, you will never be without a box. Use stiff card to make a large box and small sheets of paper to make a smaller one. Origami boxes can be used to store party favours, sweets, wedding confetti and odds and ends. A sturdy, card-folded box could be used as a simple tray to hold biscuits. Have a go, all you need is a sheet of paper and a little practice.

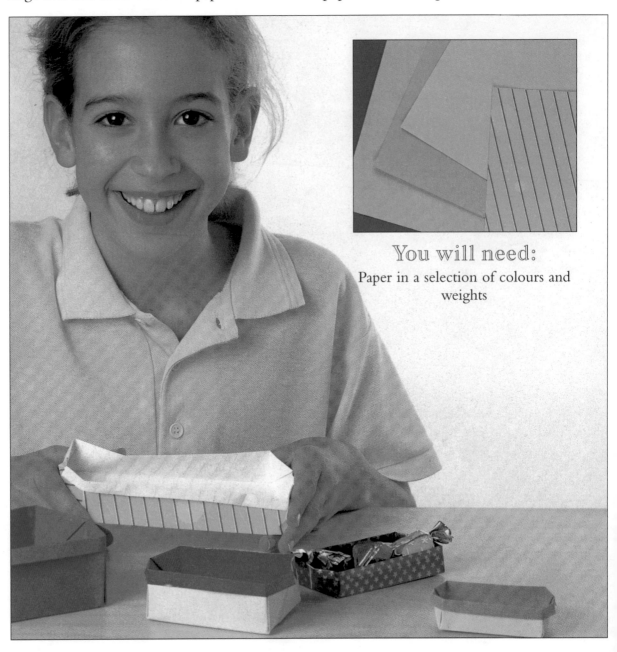

You will need:
Paper in a selection of colours and weights

1 Fold the paper in half lengthways.

2 Fold each half into the middle.

3 Make a small fold back outwards on both sides.

4 Fold in the corners and tuck them under the small fold.

5 Place your fingers in the corners and lift the box into shape.

When paper folding, be sure to press the folds firmly so they are sharp.

CARD
Desk Tidies

Use brightly coloured thin card triangles to make these desk tidies, and put them to good use holding odd paper clips or erasers. They are held together with strips of sticky tape. The containers have a simple design and their stylish shape and bright colours means they can be left plain or decorated with felt tip pens or brightly coloured strips of sticky tape.

1 Begin with a triangular sheet of of thin card. You will need to repeat the instruction at each corner.

3 Make a second fold by folding the corner back on itself. Press firmly along the fold.

2 Fold the first corner over to the opposite straight edge and press firmly along the fold.

4 When all the sides are folded, use sticky tape along the corners to hold the containers in shape.

You will need:
Thin card triangles
Sticky tape

Special Occasions

PAPER DRAGON

Chinese New Year

The Chinese New Year is a time when families enjoy reunions and gifts, as with so many of the winter festivals. The story goes that once there was a bad dragon who terrorised the people. The people were very frightened but after a while they discovered that the dragon didn't like loud noises, so they all got together and made lots of loud noises. They banged saucepan lids together, shouted and let off firecrackers to frighten him away. Nowadays there is a grand dragon procession with fireworks and many people holding up a giant paper dragon. After the event families join together to eat specially prepared meals to welcome in the New Year. They give gifts of money wrapped in red envelopes to each other. The Chinese New Year begins with a new moon, and it is also the time when the farmers gave thanks for the harvest. Have fun making your own small Chinese dragon and if there are a few of you, why not make lots of dragons so you can have your own Chinese New Year procession.

You will need:

Thin card

Felt tip pens

Glitter

Glue

Scissors

Tissue paper

Paper

Sticky tape

Two sticks

1 Draw a dragon's head onto a piece of thin card. Use felt tip pens to colour and decorate it with glitter.

4 Make the body by taking two strips of paper and folding them one over the other repeatedly to make a concertina.

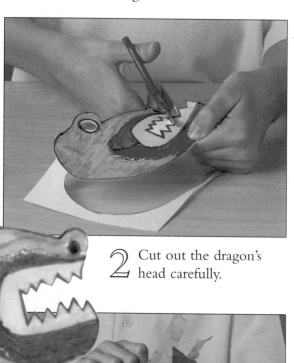

2 Cut out the dragon's head carefully.

5 Attach paper ribbons to the dragon's tail. Glue the head to the other end of the body.

3 Cut strips of tissue paper to use as ribbons. Use the glue to stick these paper ribbons to the dragon's head.

6 Use sticky tape to attach the sticks to the dragon's body. One is for the head and the other for the tail.

St. Valentine's Day

You will need a heart shaped biscuit cutter to make both the picture frames and the gingerbread hearts! Both will make great Valentine gifts to give to friends and sweethearts. The gingerbread biscuits are simple to make and can be decorated with icing or left plain.

Either way they are delicious to eat. The heart shaped picture frame has space for two pictures. It is made by rolling out the clay and using two biscuit cutters to cut the frame, one smaller than the other. A coat of varnish (or clear nail polish) will give your picture frame a professional finish.

You will need:

Air hardening clay

Heart biscuit cutter

Red paint

Paint-brush

Thread or ribbon

Glue

Recipe for gingerbread biscuits

350g plain flour

1 teaspoon baking powder

2 teaspoons ground ginger

1 teaspoon cinnamon

100g margarine

175g soft brown sugar

3 tablespoons syrup

1 egg

Icing

1 Place the flour, baking powder, ginger, cinnamon and sugar in a large bowl. Add the margarine, mix it in well with your fingertips until the mixture looks crumbly like breadcrumbs.

2 Add the sugar and syrup, mix together. Use a spoon to stir in the egg and mix.

3 Turn the mixture out onto the work surface and knead the mixture until it is smooth and well mixed. Sprinkle some flour onto the work surface and use the rolling pin to roll the mixture out to a thickness of about half a centimetre. With a heart shaped biscuit cutter cut out the shapes. Place the shapes on a baking tray and bake at 170°C, 325°F, gas mark 3 for just 10 minutes. Get an adult to help you use the oven.

4 When the gingerbread biscuits are cooked take them out of the oven and leave to stand until cold. They will harden up as they cool. When they are cool, decorate the biscuits with icing.

5 To make these picture frames you will need two biscuit cutters, one smaller than the other, and some air hardening clay. Roll out the clay and cut out two large heart shapes. One of the heart shapes will be the picture frame back. Take the smaller heart shaped biscuit cutter and cut a small heart shape out of the second heart shape. Leave the made frame pieces to dry in a warm airy place. When they have dried completely, paint them with red paint and glue them together. Place a picture of your Valentine in the frame. Use glue to secure it to the frame.

The heart-shaped frames look good enough to eat, but remember they are made from air hardening clay and are not edible!

PHOTO WALLET

Mother's Day

Make your mother this pretty photo wallet for Mother's Day. It is made with card and attractive handmade paper, but would be equally good made with decorated paper or covered with a printed fabric. A photograph of you when you were a baby would make a good cover picture rather than the cut-out flower. If you have brothers and sisters put photographs of all of you in the wallet. Use your imagination and the materials you have in your scrap box to come up with something good.

You will need:

Scissors

Paper

Card

Glue

Ribbon

Pictures

Photographs

1 You will need two equal sized pieces of thick card for the cover. Glue them onto a piece of attractive handmade paper.

4 Glue a piece of ribbon to the inside of both card cover sections. This will tie in a pretty bow to keep your wallet closed.

2 Fold the handmade paper in neatly and firmly, then glue it securely down, so that the outer edges of the two pieces of card are completely covered.

5 Stick one end of the folded page section to the inside front cover. It should cover the ribbon end too. Fix the other end of the page section to the inside back cover.

3 Now take a long piece of handmade paper and make a concertina fold. This will make the pages of the wallet.

6 Decorate the front cover with ribbon and a cut-out picture of flowers, or maybe use a picture of yourself.

GIFTS, CARDS AND DECORATIONS
Easter

In the Northern hemisphere Easter occurs in the springtime, so we have Easter bunnies, eggs and spring flowers, such as the daffodils on this delightful Easter card. It is fun to make and grandparents will enjoy receiving greeting cards at this time of year. The chocolate nests are made from breakfast cereal and melted chocolate. The tiny eggs are chocolate covered raisins, or, instead, you could use small foil covered chocolate Easter eggs. Another fun Easter activity is to make an Easter tree. This tree is made from a branch and decorated with paper Easter eggs.

You will need:

Shredded breakfast cereal

Bowl

Melted chocolate

Spoon

Foil

Bun tin

Chocolate covered raisins

1 Crumble the cereal by hand into a bowl. Check that there are no large chunks.

2 Carefully add the melted chocolate to the bowl of crumbled cereal and, using the spoon, mix well together.

3 Line a bun tin with foil and place a spoonful of the mixture into each space. Use the back of the spoon to press it down into a nest shape. Leave the shapes to harden in a cool, dry place.

4 When the nests are hard, put them on a plate and add a few chocolate covered raisins to each one. Serve up at tea time on Easter Sunday.

5 A branch decorated with paper Easter eggs will brighten up the home. Cut the Easter eggs from paper and decorate them using pencil crayons. Make a hole at one end of each egg and thread with string to hang them on the Easter tree.

6 Use coloured paper to make this Easter card. The daffodils have bright yellow paper petals and a paler yellow centre. Cut the leaves from green paper. Use glue to attach the flowers to the card.

Father's Day

This useful paperweight should be a great success as a gift on Father's Day. You will need a wooden doorknob or other small, but weighty, object to decorate. Choose a decoration that will suit his personality or hobbies; a garden-loving father would enjoy the gardening design and a DIY expert would like the woodworking tools! If he plays golf you could stick a real golf ball and tee onto the paperweight. Paint the paperweight in colours that suit the decoration - greens and browns for gardening or maybe blue, if your decoration has a watery theme.

You will need:

Wooden doorknob

Oven bake clay

Glue

Paint-brush

Paint

Varnish

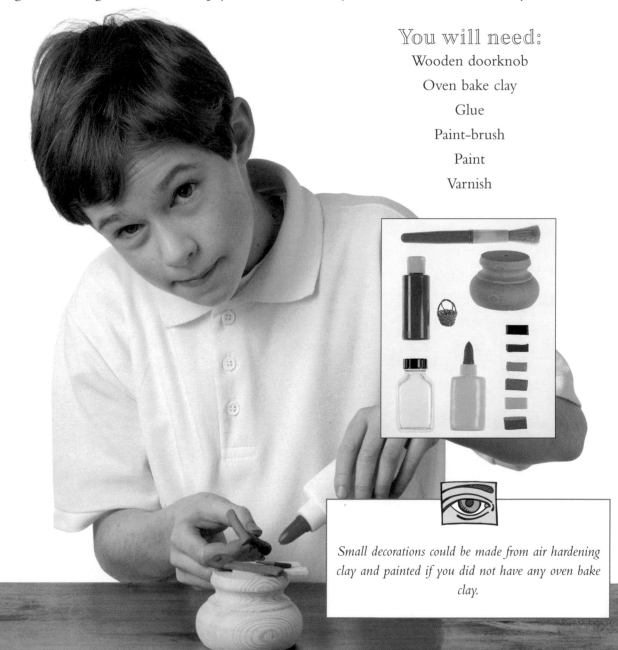

Small decorations could be made from air hardening clay and painted if you did not have any oven bake clay.

1 Use coloured oven bake clay to make the vegetables. The carrots are made from tiny sausage shapes thinned at one end with a few green pieces stuck on as stalks. To make the cabbages begin with a few small ball shapes, and flatten them into leaf shapes. When you have made a few leaves press them, one by one, onto a small ball, until you have a hearty looking cabbage. Pumpkins are made from flattened ball shapes, and the tomatoes are small red ball shapes with tiny green stalks. The miniature basket came from a florist's shop, but you could make a basket from clay. Harden the vegetables in the oven according to the manufacturer's instructions. Paint the doorknob dark green. Use strong glue to attach the vegetables and basket to the doorknob.

2 When the glue has dried brighten up the paperweight with a little red paint and then varnish the whole item to give a professional finish.

3 The doorknob has been left unpainted for this carpenter's design. Make the miniature tools from oven bake clay, baked in the oven according to the manufacturer's instructions.

4 Use glue to attach the hardened tools to the doorknob and when the glue has dried, varnish the paperweight. For a golfing father, decorate the doorknob with a golf ball and tee.

SAND AND PETAL PICTURE
Diwali

Followers of the Hindu religion celebrate many festivals. Diwali or the Festival of Light is my favourite Hindu festival. Diwali is celebrated around October/November time and is a New Year celebration. In Hindu homes the house is cleaned and decorated with coloured glitter, sand and flowers. Lots of small clay lamps are kept burning on windowsills and on doorsteps. These lights are to welcome Lakshmi, the goddess of wealth. Everyone hopes she will visit them over this period and bring good fortune for the New Year. Many Hindu homes in India have sand pictures drawn up outside their front doors to welcome visitors. Make a sand and flower picture to place in your hall during Diwali.

You will need:

Air hardening clay

Paint-brush and paint

Paper and pencil

Glue stick

Coloured sand

Flower petals

Glitter

Before you use a candle make sure you have an adult present.

1 To make your Diwali lamp you will need a ball of air hardening clay. Use your fingers to shape it into a bowl shape and press a fancy edge into the clay. When the lamp has dried, paint it in bright colours and decorate with gold or silver paint. Place a nightlight candle in the lamp and check with an adult before you light it.

2 You will need a large piece of paper. Use a pencil to sketch a flower picture onto the paper. Use a glue stick to mark the centre of the flower.

3 Pour coloured sand onto the glue mark.

4 Next use the glue stick to mark out the shape of the petals.

5 Pour coloured sand onto the glue lines.

6 When you have completed the sand picture place flower petals as a border.

7 Use glitter to add the finishing touch to your Diwali picture.

LANTERNS, GAMES AND CREATURES
Hallowe'en

Hallowe'en is a spooky time of year. Make a hollowed-out pumpkin lantern. Carve a face on one side of the pumpkin and stand it outside your home with a lit candle inside. The golden candle light will shine through the dark! For ghoulish fun try making this very squidgy Hallowe'en game. Your friends will enjoy plenty of laughs searching the green gunge for spiders and worms. The glow-in-the-dark character worm is made from oven bake glow clay. You could make some to put in trick or treat boxes. Open them in the dark to enjoy the glow!

1 Half fill a large bowl with water. Add enough food colouring to turn the water dark green. Sprinkle 3 or 4 tablespoons of wallpaper glue onto the water. Allow the wallpaper glue to sink to the bottom and then stir gently with the spoon until the mixture is sloppy and thick.

2 Add the spiders and toads and the game is ready to play. Take turns to feel through the gunge and guess which creature you are fishing out.

3 Make the cute little glow-in-the-dark worm with special oven bake glow clay. Make the body first, then form it into the worm shape. Make a number of small ball shapes in dark green and flatten them. Press them onto the worm. Make a hat and place it on the worm's head. Bake the completed model according to the manufacturer's instructions. You could stand the finished worm on a shelf as an ornament or turn him into a fridge magnet or brooch.

You will need:

Bowl

Water

Green food colouring

Wallpaper glue

A selection of plastic toads and spiders

Oven bake glow clay

Pumpkin

Knife

Candle

FESTIVAL CANDLESTICK
Hanukkah

Hanukkah is the Jewish festival of lights. It is celebrated as a reminder of the time 2000 years ago when the Jewish Temple was destroyed in battle by the Syrian king. When the battle was over the Jewish people repaired the Temple and went to light the oil lamp which burns in front of the Ark. They found they had hardly any oil, only enough for one day. But, by a miracle, the oil lasted eight days, long enough for the people to prepare more Holy oil to burn. Nowadays Jewish families celebrate Hanukkah in December for eight days, lighting a candle each day until they are all lit. Then they enjoy a time of celebration with parties, games and gifts. You can make a small Hanukkah candlestick to stand on a windowsill. Keep it lit through the festival.

1 Divide your clay into thirds. Roll two thirds out into a long rectangle. Cut out a zig-zag pattern to make the base of the candlestick. Flatten the edges of the zig-zag so that the candlestick will stand securely. The remaining third of the clay will make the candleholders. You will need one candleholder in the centre and four on each side of it.

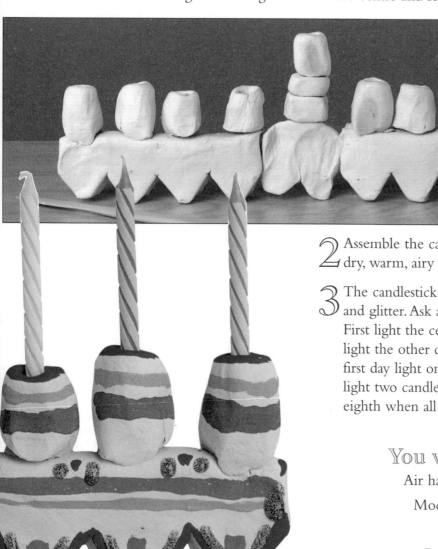

2 Assemble the candlestick and leave it in a dry, warm, airy place before decorating it.

3 The candlestick is decorated with paint and glitter. Ask an adult to help each day. First light the centre candle and use that to light the other candles day by day. On the first day light one candle, on the second light two candles and so on, until the eighth when all eight candles will be lit.

You will need:

Air hardening clay

Modelling tool

Paint

Paint-brush

Glitter

Candles

NATIVITY SCENE
Christmas Eve

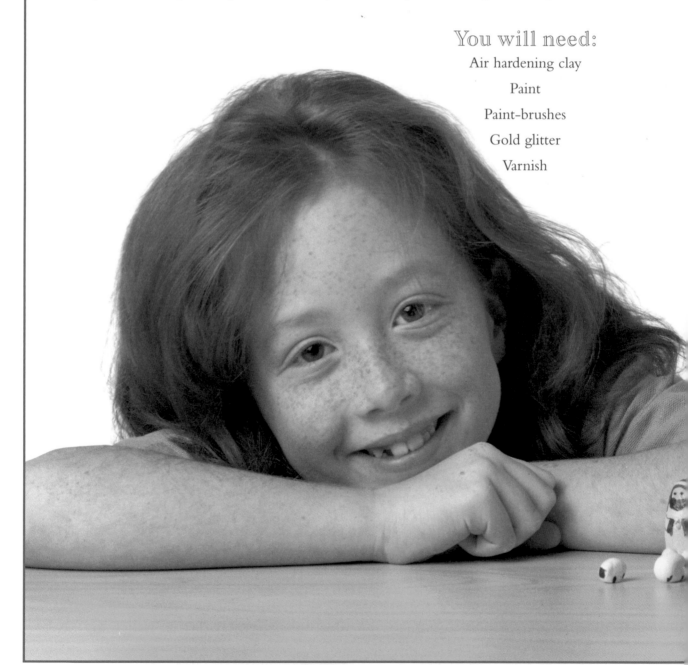

A small Nativity scene looks beautiful set up on the mantlepiece at Christmas time and reminds us of the wonderful story of Jesus' birth. This miniature scene is made from air hardening clay. The shapes are all very simple and each piece is painted carefully to create the characters. The stable is made from clay but you might want to decorate a small box as the stable and then use the box to store the Nativity scene when not on display. A Nativity scene would make a thoughtful gift for grandparents. You could keep it to use again next year.

You will need:

Air hardening clay

Paint

Paint-brushes

Gold glitter

Varnish

1 Begin by shaping the stable from a ball of clay. Next make a small cradle to hold Baby Jesus. Make a small baby shape and place it in the cradle. Mary and Joseph will be next; make Joseph a little larger than Mary. You will need a few shepherds and some shapes for sheep. Make sure these will stand up on their own. Make the three wise men last. Leave all the clay pieces to dry in a warm airy spot, then you can decorate them.

2 Follow the illustration above when painting your Nativity scene. Mary will need to have a blue cloak, and the three wise men should have a bit of gold glitter sparkling on them somewhere. Paint the sheep white with black faces and legs. When the scene is all painted allow the pieces to dry, then varnish them.

3 Joseph, Mary and Baby Jesus in the manger: a Christmas scene to remind us of the real reason behind Christmas.

CRACKERS
Christmas Day

Home made Christmas crackers are one of the many things you can make in advance in preparation for Christmas. Fill them with paper hats, jokes (good ones!) and small gifts which you could make, such as necklaces or small brooches or badges. Paper hats are easy to make from tissue paper. You will need to fold them up small so they fit in the crackers. The snaps are available from craft shops. You might want to make a special cracker for a grandparent or friend you won't be seeing over the Christmas season. Send it to them through the post so that they can pull it while they are enjoying their Christmas dinner.

You will need:
Tissue paper, for hat and cracker

Scissors

Thin card

Sticky tape

Small gift to put inside the cracker

Snaps

Glue

Glitter

You could use the central cardboard cylinder from a roll of toilet paper to shape your crackers.

1 Before you make the cracker you will need to make a tissue paper hat. Use your own head to make a standard size hat. If you are making the hat to fit an adult-head, make it a little larger. Cut a zig-zag shape along one side, and glue the two short edges together.

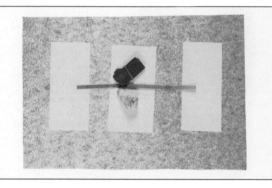

2 To make the cracker you will need a sheet of tissue paper measuring 40cm x 20cm and three pieces of thin card measuring 14cm x 8cm. Add a snap, a paper hat tightly folded, and a small gift.

3 Roll the pieces of thin card into cylinder shapes. Hold them in place with sticky tape. Run the snap through the cylinders and place the hat and gift in the central cylinder.

4 Roll the tissue paper around the cylinders and use thread to tie in between them. Pull up the thread firmly to create the cracker shape. Remove the two end cylinders and trim any excess paper away.

5 The cracker is ready to decorate. Use glitter and glue on a seasonal picture.

CAKES

Special Days

These novelty cakes look great on a party table and would make a surprise birthday gift to take to a party. The icing is simply rolled out with a rolling pin then placed over the cake. The decorative pieces are cut using biscuit cutters which come in so many shapes and sizes you are sure to find one to suit the style of cake you want to make. Use a bought-in sponge cake to ice or make your own. Ask an adult for help when you use the cooker.

Sponge cake:

75gm self raising flour

75gm castor sugar

75gm margarine

2 eggs

1 tablespoon water

1 Sieve some icing sugar onto your work surface so that the icing doesn't stick to it and roll out the icing to about half a centimetre thickness.

2 Roll the icing over the rolling pin and, lifting it gently, transfer it to the cake. Drape it over the cake and carefully remove the rolling pin.

3 Gently press the icing over the cake. Cut away any excess icing with a knife. Use a clean cloth to wipe away any icing sugar.

4 Roll out some red icing and use a biscuit cutter to cut out the star shapes. Moisten the back of the stars with a little water and press them gently onto the iced cake.

5 Use different shaped biscuit cutters to create different styles of cake. Green frogs, red stars or blue fish could be cut out and decorated further with silver balls or edible felt tip colours. Have fun creating your own designs to suit different occasions.

You will need

Sponge cakes to ice

Icing sugar

Rolling pin

Easy-roll icing

Knife

Clean cloth

Small sieve

Biscuit cutters

A little water and a pastry brush

Make your own Craft Box

It is a good idea to store all your craft materials in one place. This keeps things tidy and you always know where your stuff is. You could decorate a large sturdy box and use that. When you have finished working on a project, clean up your equipment and return everything to the box. When you have a spare moment you will be able to get straight down to being creative with all your materials to hand.

A craft box can be made especially useful if you also store found materials in it; things like feathers you may find in the garden or nice shaped pebbles to paint. You can save empty boxes and cans to recycle into interesting birthday or Christmas gifts when you have time. Coloured paper is very useful – save used wrapping paper and ribbon. You may want to iron the paper with a cool iron to flatten it ready for reuse.

Plenty of useful craft materials can be found in the summer, interesting seed heads from the garden, and flowers to press. A few twigs and sticks tidily held together with a rubber band could come in useful if a younger sister needs a new piece of furniture for her doll's house. Ice-cream sticks should be washed, dried, and saved for later. Enjoy collecting interesting materials to recycle into useful gifts, games, and crafts.

Measurements & Recipes

Length

cm	ins
2.5	1
5	2
7.6	3
10	4
12.7	5
15	6
17.7	7
20	8
22.8	9
25.4	10

Weight

oz	grams
1	30
3	75
6	175
8	250

Glitter Glue
Glitter
PVA Glue

Mix equal quantities of glitter and glue. Use a spatula to spread the glitter glue on art work and store it in a tub with an airtight lid.

Temperature	
Fahrenheit	**Centigrade**
250–300	120–150
300–350	150–175
350–375	175–190
375–400	190–200
400–425	200–220

Salt and Flour Dough
2 cups flour
1 cup salt
1 cup water

Mix the ingredients with
a wooden spoon. When
the mixture begins to
form a ball use your hands
to knead it to a smooth
modelling consistency.

Acknowledgements

The publishers would like to thank the children listed below for appearing in the photographs in this book.

Fola Akinwumi

Rebecca Anderson

Luke Anderson

Joe Bacon

Matthew Bames-Smith

Natasha Bames-Smith

Laura Bannister

Lauren Barrett

Jenny Beacock

Lillie Berger

Alex Bermingham

Harriet Bolton

Scarlett Bolton

Alice Bolton

Peter Bolton

Ben Boyd

William Brown

Joshua Brown

Leanne Marie Claydon

Killian Collender

Tim Cutting

Donal Edwards

Stephanie Everett

Hazel Garvie-Cook

Joshua George

Katie George

Africa Green

James Grimsaw

Francesca Hails

Joshua Hails

David Haines

Chloe Hannan

Anna Harrington

Lucy Harrington

Ben Howard

Cordell Jackson

Ben Kelvin

Rebecca Kelvin

Jessica Kilpatrick

Jack Kilpatrick

Charlie Mackrill

Abigail Mackrill

James McDonald

Kirsty McDonald

Samuel McGill

Puspita McKenzie

David Merriam

Ned Miles

Vicky Miller

Benedict O'Neill

Luke O'Neill

Ryan Oyeyemi

Holly Rayson

Daisy Rayson

Natalie Roberts

Luke Rutter

Lucy Sales

Eriko Sato

Jamie Saunter

Tariq Sayfoo

Shirine Sayfoo

Julia Smerdon

Katie Smerdon

Lizzie Smith

Christopher Stacey

Emma Stacey

Oliver Sword

Harriet Thomas

Jessica Thurbourn

Helen Thurlow

Rebecca Tomlinson

Joanna Tomlinson

Ava Wallington-Wallis

Sebina Wallis-King

Charlie Wapshott

Tom Wapshott

Andrew Waterhouse

Frances Waterhouse